Third

HULL
The Heavenly Pottery

By
Joan Gray Hull

An Alphabetical, Numerical, Pictorial, Pocket Size
Price Guide for Hull Pottery Lovers

Darlene Kutzler, Photographer

Copyright
1993

Joan Gray Hull
ISBN
0-9627078-2-1

Printed by
Creative Printing
173 Second S.W.
Huron, SD 57350

Additional copies may be
ordered from

Joan Gray Hull
1376 Nevada SW
Huron, SD 57350
Telephone: 605-352-1685

$19.95 plus $1.05 postage & handling

DEDICATION

This book is dedicated to the memory of my late husband, Vernon W. (Bill) Hull, who gave me his name, his love, and our four children: Judy Jensen, Julie DuMay, Cathy Nelson, and Connie Somsen.

CONTENTS

ACKNOWLEDGEMENTS.. 5
TRADEMARKS 6
LABELS... 7
PRICING.. 7
ACME 8
ADVERTISING PLAQUES... 10
BLOSSOM FLITE 11
BLUE BIRD & CONVENTIONAL ROSE CEREAL WARE...... 13
BOW KNOT 14
BUTTERFLY... 16
CALLA LILLY/JACK-IN-THE-PULPIT................................. 18
CAPRI 20
CINDERELLA/BLOSSOM & BOUQUET............................. 21
CLASSIC.. 22
CLOCKS 23
CONTINENTAL 24
COOKIE JAR/DUCK... 24
CRAB APPLE.. 26
CRESCENT 27
CRESTONE 28
DEBONAIR 29
DOGWOOD/WILDROSE... 30
EBB TIDE.. 32
FANTASY... 33
FIESTA.. 34
FLORAL 35
GRANADA/MARDI GRAS... 36
HEARTLAND.. 37
HERITAGE (AVACADO) 37
HOUSE & GARDEN.. 38
IMPERIAL, NOVELTY, MISC... 42
IRIS/NARCISSUS... 56
LAMPS.. 58
LEEDS BOTTLES 61
LITTLE RED RIDING HOOD 62
LUSTERWARE 71
MAGNOLIA 72
MARQUEST... 76
MORNING GLORY.. 77
NULINE BAK-SERVE 78
OLD SPICE.. 79
OPEN ROSE/CAMELLIA... 84
ORCHID 84
PAGODA.. 86

PARCHMENT & PINE 86
PINECONE 87
POPPY 88
RAINBOW 90
ROSELLA 91
ROYAL 92
SAMPLES/EXPERIMENTALS 93
SERENADE 96
STONEWARE (EARLY ART) 97
STONEWARE (EARLY UTILITY) 98
SUN GLOW 102
SUPREME 103
THISTLE 103
TILE 104
TOKAY/TUSCANY 106
TROPICANA 107
TULIP (SUENO) 108
WATER LILY 110
WILDFLOWER 112
WOODLAND 117
ZANE GREY 120
HAND PAINTED DINNERWARE 121
HISTORY 122
BIBLIOGRAPHY 124
ABOUT THE AUTHOR 125
INDEX 126
ADVERTISING 128

Mr. Byron E. Hull, former Vice President of the Hull Pottery Company, and the author, Joan Gray Hull, taken in front of the Hull factory in Crooksville, Ohio in July, 1985. Mr. Hull died August 7, 1992, the last of the Hull brothers, thus ending the era of the Hull Pottery Company.

It took years of encouragement from the many Hull collectors and dealers across the country before I actually began the undertaking of "HULL THE HEAVENLY POTTERY".

I am amazed at the number of letters and calls I have received from all over the United States from people who tell me how much they love the alphabetical, numerical pocket sized price guide of the First Edition of "HULL, THE HEAVENLY POTTERY". I am so happy to know that the book is as much desired by you as I thought it would be. I appreciate each letter or call that you have taken the time to send me.

I began collecting after my husbands death when a friend, Joy Johnson, bought a piece of Hull at a rummage sale and gave it to me saying, "With a name like Hull, you should be collecting it." The suggestion took and I began searching antique shops and flea markets of the first time in my life. (I highly recommend new hobbies for grief therapy.) Collecting has changed my life. After 18 years, I now own approximately 2000 pieces of this lovely pottery.

My deep appreciation goes to my photographer, Darlene Kutzler for her hard work. Without Dee Konyha, the First Edition could never have been printed. John Burks sent a number of updated pictures for the Second Edition. The Third Edition is greatly enhanced by pictures from Gayle McGooden's extensive collection.

HULL THE HEAVENLY POTTERY is designed to be a price guide only. Avid Hull Collectors should have Robert's "ULTIMATE ENCYCLOPEDIA OF HULL POTTERY" for a complete History of the company including trademarks and labels. HULL THE HEAVENLY POTTERY is photographed mostly from my personal collection. I show only a token amount of the 13 dinnerware molds produced by Hull. Hull collectors are urged to add Barbara Burke's "A GUIDE TO THE HULL POTTERY COMPANY DINNERWARE LINES" to their book collection.

I want to acknowledge a few of the people who have helped with the publishing of the Third Edition. Space does not permit me to name them all but each person is deeply appreciated: Mary Ann Boddy, Fran Bolles, Barbara Burke, John Burks, Jackie Bush, Charles Endres, Marv Faughender, Fenner's, Steve & Lori Friend, C.J. Ghan, Debbie Hefflinger, Denny Huffman, LaDonna Johnson, Steve Johnson, Juan Kleinhofer, Dee Konyha, Gayle McGooden, Jewelyn Nichols, Linda Puryea, Mark Supnick, Lowell Thomas, Preston Ver Meer, & Joe Yonis.

TRADEMARKS

Hull's number system is extensive and very confusing to the new collector. Most designs bear a different type of trademark. Some Stoneware pottery is marked with a number and an (H) or a ⟨H⟩. The popular matte finished Hull pieces are also marked in a number of ways: some are in raised letters, some incised, some blocked, and some are in script writing. Kitchenware items' trademarks usually include the words Oven Proof. Molds manufactured after 1950 are often in script writing. The most modern florist planter type molds often show Hull written with the small "h".

Letters, as well as numbers, are used on some designs to help the collector identify the pattern.

LABELS

The lucky collector may find pieces of Hull pottery with the original label still on the vase. Most of the labels are the triangle shaped label in black with the words Hull Pottery in silver or gold, or the round label bearing a picture of a Potter-at-Wheel and the words Hull Pottery Crooksville, Ohio printed in silver or gold. Other labels with other markings and/or colors can be found. Labels should add $5 to $10 value to each vase depending on the condition of the label.

PRICING

Collectors and dealers from New York to Florida, from California to Idaho, Michigan, Nebraska, and many points in between have sent me their price lists to be averaged. I've used mean, mode, and median to arrive at the figures. I also averaged in prices that I have seen in the **Antique Trader** this past year. A few pieces had such variation in the pricing, that I have listed both the high and low suggested price range. Prices will be affected by the condition of the vase, labels, gold trim, unusual finishes, and other variables.

Since the First Edition of HULL THE HEAVENLY POTTERY, I feel some prices of Hull have become almost outrageous. Prices in Bowknot, Little Red Riding Hood, and the Wildflower numbered series have climbed 25% to over 100% of the published prices. As a collector, I don't see how these prices can continue to rise at such rates or most of us will not be able to afford to add to our lovely collections.

Other items that seem to have risen drastically are the larger vase, pitchers, and baskets. I understand these price increases in the rarer hard to find pieces. The deeper we are into collecting and research of Hull, the more we understand which pieces are the rarest and command the higher prices. As always, some prices will seem too high in one area and too low in another. Prices are to be used only as a guide. The owner does not have to sell a piece of pottery for any less than he wishes. By the same token, the buyer does not have to buy any item that he considers over priced.

The Acme Pottery Company was formed in 1903 and began producing pieces until the Hull plant was formed in 1907.

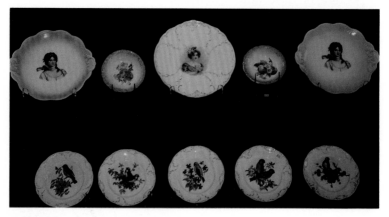

Row 1

1. Acme Porcelain Crooksville plate, scroll stamp, 11" $175
2. Acme Porcelain fruit bowl, eagle stamp, 5 1/2"...$65
3. Acme Porcelain plate, eagle stamp, 10 1/2".......$135
4. Acme Porcelain fruit bowl, eagle stamp, 5 1/2"...$65
5. Acme Porcelain Crooksville plate, scroll stamp, 11"...$175

Row 2

1. Acme Porcelain bird plates, eagle stamp, 7 1/2"..$95

The Acme Pottery Co. 13" bowl marked with eagle stamp, $95.

This Acme berry set was shown at the First Annual Hull Pottery Festival in Crooksville, Ohio in 1992. The owner priced it at $1000.

Row 1
1. Acme covered casserole...$125
2. Acme platter...$175
3. Acme salad plate $65
4. Acme soup bowl..$65

The advertising signs are so rare that pricing is very difficult. I have seen them range from $2500 up. It is a lucky collector who owns one of the three advertising pieces shown.

The small plaques are 5 1/2" x 2 1/4". The large plaque is 11" x 5 1/4"

Little Red Riding Hood advertising plaque 12" x 6 1/2"

BLOSSOM FLITE

A pink high gloss and floral design with black or blue lattice markings decorate the Hull Blossom Flite pattern. Blossom Flite was produced by Hull in the middle 1950's.

Row 1

1. T1 6" honey jug..$50
2. T2 6" basket..$50
Page 12. T3 81/2" pitcher..$100
3. T4 8 1/2" basket..$100

Row 2

1. T6 10 1/2" cornucopia $85
2. T7 9 1/2" vase $85
3. T8 8 1/4" x 9 1/4" basket....................................$115
NP. T9 10" low basket..$125

Row 3

1. T10 16 1/2" x 6 3/4" console bowl........................$95
2. T11 3 1/4" candleholders pr. $50

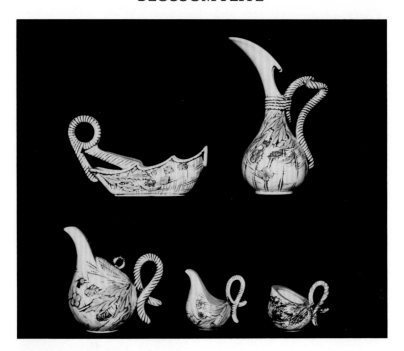

Row 1

1. T12 10 1/2" boat flower bowl $75
1. T13 12 1/2" pitcher..$135

Row 2

1. T14 8" teapot $85
2. T15 creamer...$40
3. T16 sugar (no lid) $40

1. Blossom Flite pitcher mold with pine cone & butterfly decoration
2. T3 8 1/2" pitcher
3. Butterfly ashtray
4. Ash tray made of Butterfly mold with Blossom Flite Pattern

BLUEBIRD CEREAL WARE

Cereal Ware was produced by Hull from 1915 to 1935, and was sold in sets or individually.

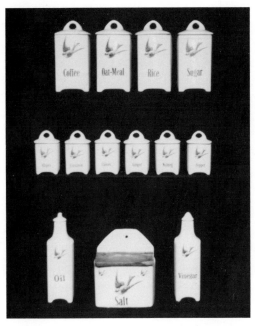

Row 1 Canisters, each $100
Row 2 Spice jars, each $75
Row 3 Cruet, each...$150
        Salt Box $175

CONVENTIONAL ROSE CEREAL WARE

Canisters, each...$100

BOW KNOT

Manufactured in late forties, Bow Knot is a favorite in many collections. This matte-finished pattern is made in pastel pink/blue or turquoise/blue. Most pieces feature a ribbon bow.

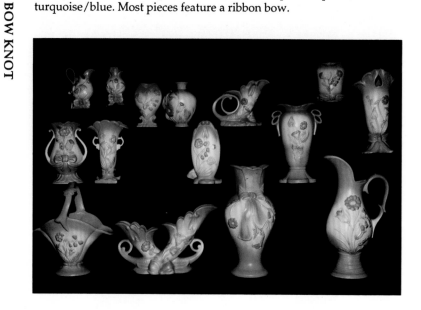

Row 1

1. B-1 5 1/2" pitcher..$165
2. B-2 5" vase..$145
3. B-3 5 1/2" vase..$145
4. B-4 5 1/2" vase..$145
5. B-5 7 1/2" cornucopia...$145
6. B-6 6 1/2" planter/saucer..$165

Row 2

1. B-7 8 1/2" vase..$185
2. B-8 8 1/2" vase..$185
3. B-9 8 1/2" vase..$185
4. B-10 10 1/2" vase...$325
5. B-11 10 1/2" vase...$335

Row 3

1. B-12 10 1/2" basket..$650
2. B-13 13 1/2" double cornucopia..$225
3. B-14 12 1/2" vase...$1200
4. B-15 13 1/2 pitcher..$1300

Row 1
1. B-16 13 1/2" console bowl $300
2. B-17 4" candleholders pr. $175
3. B-18 5 3/4" jardiniere $165
4. B-19 9 3/8" jardiniere $900

Row 2
1. B-20 6" teapot...$400
2. B-21 4" creamer..$150
3. B-22 4" sugar (lid missing)...$150
4. B-24 6" wall planter cup & saucer $195
5. B-25 6 1/2" basket..$225

Row 3
1. B-26 6" wall planter pitcher $195
2. B-27 8" wall planter whisk broom $195
3. B-28 10" plate/plaque...$1200
4. B-29 12" basket..$1800
5. Unmarked wall pocket iron $195

Rare B-2 painted in shades of tan and brown.

The first B-1 vase is a reproduction. Notice it is slightly smaller and the design is not as clear as the original.

BUTTERFLY

The Hull Butterfly pattern was manufactured in the middle 1950's. Colors were ivory smooth matte finish or white pebble effect, both featuring pink, black, and blue butterflies.

Row 1
1. B1 6" pitcher...$40
2. B2 6" small cornucopia $35
3. B3 7" ashtray $50
4. B4 6" bon bon dish $35
5. B5 6" jardiniere..$45
6. B6 5 1/2" candy dish..$45

Row 2
1. B7 9 3/4" rectangular bowl.....................................$45
2. B8 12 3/4" window box..$45
3. B9 9" vase..$50
4. B10 7" vase..$50

Row 3
1. B11 8 3/4" pitcher...$95
2. B12 10 1/2" cornucopia $75
3. B13 8" basket $125

Row 1

1. B14 10 1/2" vase $75
2. B15 13 1/2" Pitcher..$160
3. B16 10 1/2" fruit bowl $100
4. B17 10 1/2" basket...$300
5. B24 lavabo top $100
6. B25 lavabo bottom...$100

Row 2

1. B18 teapot...$135
2. B19 creamer...$50
3. B20 sugar with lid $50
4. B21 console bowl...$100
5. B22 candleholder...$35
6. B23 11 1/2" serving tray..$100

CALLA LILY/JACK IN THE PULPIT

The Calla Lily design is often referred to as Jack-in-the-Pulpit. It was manufactured in the late 1930's. The matte colors are in numerous shades of blues, yellows, greens, pinks, and rusts in various combinations.

Row 1
1. 500/32 8" bowl..$125
2. 500/32 10" bowl..$160
3. 500/33 6" vase..$95
4. 500/33 8" vase..$125
5. 501/33 6" vase..$95

Row 2
1. 502/33 6" vase..$95
2. 503/33 6" vase..$95
3. 504 6" vase..$95
4. 505 6" vase..$95
5. 506 10" pitcher...$275

Row 3
1. 510/33 8" vase..$125
2. 520/33 6" vase..$95
3. 520/33 8" vase..$125
4. 520/33 10" vase..$300
5. 530/33 5" vase..$80

Row 1
1. 530/33 7" vase..$110
2. 530/33 9" vase..$300
3. 540/33 6" vase..$95
NP. 550/33 5" vase...$95
4. 550/33 7 1/2" vase $125
5. 560/33 8" vase..$250
6. 560/33 10" vase..$300

Row 2
1. 570/33 8" cornucopia...$100
2. 591 7" jardiniere...$275
3. 2 1/4" unmarked candleholders, pr. $150
4. 590/33 13" x 4" console bowl..............................$275

Row 3
1. 592 6" flower pot..$125
2. 920/33-2 5" unknown design $50
3. 920/33-3 5" unknown design $50
4. 920/33-4 5" unknown design $50
5. 930/33, 5" unknown design...................................$50

Manufactured in the early 1960's, Capri has a rough texture. It is finished in shades of Coral or Seagreen.

NP. C14 4" vase...$20
NP. C15 5 3/4" pedestal vase $25
NP. C21 3" swan planter $15
NP. C23 8 1/2" swan planter (See Page 53, Picture 3, Row 2, No. 1).......$35
NP. C28 9 3/4" vase $40
NP. C29 12" vase...$60
NP. C38 6 3/4" basket (See Page 44, Row 2, No. 1) $30

Row 1
  1. C44 4 1/4" jardiniere...$20
NP. C45 4 1/4" x 6" ribbed pedestal flower bowl...$25
  2. C46 4 1/2" x 8" flower bowl...................................$30
  3. C47 5 1/4" x 8" round flower bowl......................$35
NP. C47C 5 1/4" x 8" bon bon bowl (same as above with lid)...$40
Row 2
  1. C48 12 1/4" x 5 1/2" basket $50
  2. C49 5 3/4" lion head goblet $30
NP. C50 9" lion head goblet.......................................$40
  3. C52 10" x 7 1/2" ash tray $40
NP. C57 14 1/2" open front hanging basket vase...$75
                  (see page 25 No. C57)
NP. C58 13 3/4" vase $65
NP. C59 15" vase...$75
NP. C62 5 1/2" compote...$25
NP. C62C 8 1/2" candy dish with lid (See Page 25 No. C62C) .$35
  4. C63 14" caladium leaf dish................................$65
NP. C67 4" square footed planter/candleholder....$20
NP. C68 8 1/2" rectangular flower dish...................$30
Row 3
  1. C80 llama planter $75
  2. C81 twin swan planter $65
  3. C87 12" pine cone pitcher....................................$75
NP. C314 flying duck planter...................................$45

(*NP - not pictured)

Cinderella is the trademark name for the kitchen items called Blossom with a single flower, and Bouquet with a pink, yellow, and blue flower. These items were manufactured late in the 1940's and into the 1950's. Items include pitchers, bowls, grease jars, and salt and pepper shaker.

Row 1
mixing bowl 7 1/2" $40
mixing bowl 9 1/2" $60

Row 2
1. teapot $95
2. creamer $30
3. milk pitcher 16 oz. $45

This cookie jar is valued at $100.

CLASSIC

The classic line of Hull pottery was manufactured for chain store use in the 1950's. Classic colors were glossy pink or ivory over a rough surface with a single pink or blue flower.

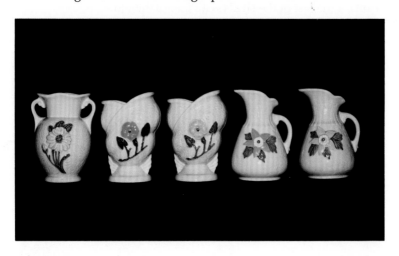

Row 1
1. 4-6" vase...$25
2. & 3. 5-6" vases...$25
4. & 5. 6-6" pitchers $25

Hull pottery shells for wall clocks were made between 1936 and 1945. There were only a few made as foreign competition undercut the market. Hull employees were among the last ones to obtain the last of the shells with clocks therein.

Row 1

1. Clock, movement by Lanshire ....$200-$400
2. Clock, movement by Sessions.....................$200-$450
3. Clock, movement by Sessions.....................$200-$450

Bluebird clock by Sessions painted in the brilliant shades of Hull's Little Red Riding Hood items -- $200 - $450.

CONTINENTAL

Continental is a very modern pottery, manufactured in the late 1950's with high gloss finish and stripes. Continental is in three colors: Evergreen, Persimmon and Mountain Blue.

Row 1

NP. A1 8" ash tray $35
NP. A3 12" rectangular ash tray $60
NP. A20 10" ash tray with pen $50
1. C28 9 3/4" vase $50
2. C29 12" vase $75
3. C51 15 1/2" x 3 1/4" flower dish $55
NP. C52 10" x 7 1/4" ash tray $55
4. C53 8 1/2" vase $45
5. C54 12 1/2" vase $60
6. C55 12 1/2" basket $125

Row 2

1. C56 12 1/2" pitcher $135
2. C57 14 1/2" open front (hanging basket) vase $95
3. C58 13 3/4" vase $95
4. C59 15" vase $100
NP. C60 15" pedestal vase $100
5. & 6. C61 10" vase/candleholders $55

Row 3

1. C62 8 1/4" candy dish $40
NP. C63 14" caladium leaf (see page 20, row 2) $75
2. C64 10" open front hanging basket) vase $70
3. C66 9 1/2" bud vase $40
4. C67 4" square planter/candleholder $25
5. C68 8 1/2" x 4 1/2" rectangular planter $25
NP. C69 9 1/4" footed flower bowl $50
6. C70 13 1/4" console/candleholder bowl $75

(*NP. - not pictured)

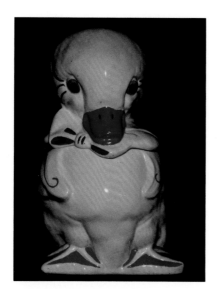

COOKIE JAR/DUCK
No. 966 Cookie Jar – $125

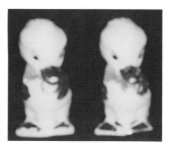

SALT & PEPPER
DUCK SET – $50.

CRAB APPLE

The Crab Apple design seems to be a difficult pattern for collectors to find. It was manufactured in the mid 1930's in 18 known molds of vases in shades of blue, tan, or white.

Row 1

1. 3" vase $35
2. 4" vase $45
3. 5" vase $60
4. 6" vase $75
5. 5" vase $60

Row 2

1. 7" vase $105
2. 7" vase $125
3. 8" vase $125
4. 8" vase $125
5. 9" vase $150

Row 3

1. 4" jardiniere $45
   N.P. 6" jardiniere $75
2. 6 1/2" jardiniere..$80
3. 8" jardiniere..$150
4. 8 1/2" flower bowl $175
5. 6" pot and saucer..$200
   N.P. 6" Hanging basket $200
   N.P. 7" Hanging basket $200

CRESCENT

Crescent kitchen items were made in the 1950's featuring crescent handles. Items were manufactured in shades of chartreuse/dark green and shades of brick/rose.

NP. B-1 5 1/2" bowl		$10
NP. B-1 7 1/2" bowl		$15
NP. B-1 9 1/2" bowl		$20

Picture - Row 1

1. B-2 10" casserole/lid		$40
NP. B-4 3 1/2" shaker		$10
NP. B-5 3 1/2" shaker		$10
2. B-7 5 1/2" casserole/lid		$20
3. B-8 9 1/2" cookie jar/lid		$65

Row 2

1. B-13 7 1/2" teapot/lid		$65
2. B-14 4 1/2" sugar/lid		$20
3. B-15 4 1/4" creamer		$20
4. B-14 4 1/4" sugar/lid		$20
5. B-15 4 1/4" creamer		$20

This Crab Apple vase had the following message imprinted on the bottom:

SAMPLE

The A & E Hull Pottery Co.
Crooksville, Ohio

STYLE NO _____

DECORATIONS _____

SIZE_____ 7"_____

CRESTONE

Crestone tableware dishes are a beautiful turquoise with white foam edge. Thirty-five pieces have been listed by premium catalogs.

Row 1
1. 2 cup carafe/lid..$50
2. 8 cup coffee pot/lid...$60
3. 8 oz. creamer..$20
4. 8 oz. sugar...$20

Row 2
1. cereal bowl...$ 5
2. 9 oz. mug...$ 5
3. 7 oz. cup & saucer...$10
4. 10 1/4" dinner plate...$10
5. 7 1/2" salad or dessert plate...$ 5

Debonair kitchenware was made in the 1950's in stripes and shades of glossy pink and gray or in solid colors.

Row 1

1. 01 3 piece mixing bowl set (shown 7").............$15, $25, $35
NP. 02 covered casserole $35
2. 04 salt shaker $10
3. 05 pepper shaker...$10
4. 06 pitcher...$25
NP. 07 individual covered caserole...................................$10
NP. 08 covered cookie jar $50
NP. 010 cereal/salad bowl $5

Row 2

1. 013 coffee/tea pot..$40
2. 014 creamer...$10
3. 015 covered sugar $10
4. 016 mug..$10

Row 3

1. 017 partitioned dutch oven/cover $40

(*NP - not pictured)

DOGWOOD/WILD ROSE

Dogwood or Wild Rose, manufactured in the middle 1940's is one of the lovely matte finish designs. The vases come in shades of peach, pink/blue, or turquoise/peach.

Row 1

1. 501 7 1/2" basket...$265
2. 502 6 1/2" suspended vase $150
3. 503 8 1/2" vase $95

Row 2

1. 504 8 1/2" vase $95
2. 505 7" pitcher $225
3. 506 11 1/2" pitcher..$300
4. 507 5 1/2" teapot & lid $300

(without lid it was called a watering can)

Row 3

1. 508 10 1/2" window box $150
2. 509 6 1/2" vase $85
3. 510 10 1/2" vase $200

Row 1
1. 511 11 1/2" cornucopia...$200
2. 512 4" candleholders pr.......................................$150

Row 2
1. 513 6 1/2" vase $100
2. 514 4" jardiniere...$75
3. 515 8 1/2" vase $50
4. 516 4 3/4" vase $55
5. 517 4 3/4" vase $55

Row 3
1. 519 13 1/2" pitcher..$700
2. 520 4 3/4" pitcher..$95
3. 521 7" low bowl $100
4. 522 4" cornucopia..$55

EBB TIDE

Manufactured in the middle 1950's, Ebb Tide shapes are of fish and shells in shades of chartreuse/wine and shrimp/turquoise.

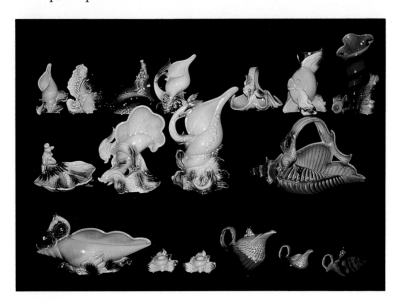

Row 1

1. E-1 7" bud vase..$55
2. E-2 7" twin fish vase $75
3. E-3 7 1/2" cornucopia with mermaid $175
4. E-4 8 1/4" pitcher vase $95
5. E-5 9 1/8" basket $95
6. E-6 9 1/4" angel fish vase......................................$95
7. E-7 11" fish vase..$125

Row 2

1. E-8 ash tray with mermaid $150
2. E-9 11 3/4" cornucopia..$125
3. E-10 13" pitcher..$175
4. E-11 16 1/2" basket $200

Row 3

1. E-12 15 3/4" snail console bowl..........................$150
2. E-13 candleholders pr...$75
3. E-14 teapot/lid $165
4. E-15 creamer $45
5. E-16 sugar/lid $45

Fantasy molds were made in the late 1950's in pink, blue, and black. Some pieces are finished with a foam edge.

Row 1
   1. small rectangular planter $20
   2. 19 very large heart-shaped ash tray planter........$60
   3. 35 rectangular planter..$20

Row 2
   1. 57 pedestal vase..$40
   2. 73 vase 9 1/2 ....$45
   3. 74 window box $45

Row 3
   1. 76 pedestal planter..$35
   2. 77 pedestal fruit bowl...$100
   3. 78 tall candleholders...$65

The Ebb Tide mermaid mold used on E3 &E8 was given to the Ohio Ceramic Center when the Hull Pottery Company closed. This mermaid was painted by Nancy Dennis and sold at the Ohio Ceramic Center in 1992.

Fiesta is a mid 1950's glossy chain store item decorated in fruits, flowers, animals, and other designs.

No. 48 8 3/4" pitcher $55

Row 1
1. 43 pedestal planter with rose design....................$35
2. 44 basket with squirrel design.............................$30
3. 45 pedestal vase with strawberry design $45
4. 46 pedestal planter with strawberry design........$50

Row 2
1. 49 cornucopia with grape design 8 1/2 ....$50
2. 50 vase with deer design..$55
3. 52 12" planter with leaves and berries $45

Row 3
1. 78 12" leaf shaped planter $55
2. 112 10" leaf and grape wall planter $45
3. 116 6" rectangular vase with leaves.....................$35
4. 403 scalloped planter $45

Floral is a kitchen ware line manufactured in the early 1950's featuring a yellow sunflower or daisy type flower.

Row 1

1. 40 5" mixing bowl...$10
2. 40 6" mixing bowl...$15
3. 40 7" mixing bowl...$20
4. 40 8" mixing bowl...$25
5. 40 9" mixing bowl...$30
NP. 41 9" lipped mixing bowl $40
NP. 42 7 1/2" covered casserole..............................$40
NP. 43 5 3/4" covered grease dish...........................$35

Row 2

1. 44 3 1/2" salt & pepper...$25
2. 46 1 quart pitcher..$40
NP. 47 casserole with lid...$45
3. 48 8 1/4" cookie jar and lid $50
4. 49 10" salad bowl..$45
NP. 50 6" cereal bowl...$ 5
NP. 79 6 1/2" basket..$65

(*NP. - not pictured)

Granada/Mardi Gras vases were designed for ten cent store sales. Manufactured in the 1940's and 1950's. The vases are white, shades of pink/blue, or tans that have embossed flowers.

Row 1
   1. 31 10" pitcher.................$115
   2. 32 8" basket....................$125
   3. 33 5 1/2 teapot $200

Row 2
   1. 47 9" vase $45
   2. 48 9" vase $45
   3. 49 9" vase $45

Row 3
   1. 62-8" Morning Glory
       basket $400
   2. 66 -11" Morning Glory
       pitcher $400
   3. 65-8" basket.....................$125
   4. 66-10" pitcher $125
   5. 215-9" vase $45

61 - 9" Morning Glory vase – $200

219 - 9" vase – $45

The Heartland canister set and tea set was purchased by John Burks from the Hull factory in Crooksville in 1984-85.

HERITAGEWARE/AVACADO

Heritageware kitchenware pieces were manufactured in the late 1950's. House & Garden molds were used to make the Heritageware pieces. Some feel this shade of green pottery was considered one of the colors in the Rainbow line.

Row 1
1. handled casserole/lid $15
2. creamer $15
3. sugar/lid $15
4. cup and saucer $15

Row 2
1. milk pitcher $35
2. dinner plate $10
3. salad plate $5

HOUSE & GARDEN

House and Garden is the name used for the brown serving dishes produced from the 1960's until the closing of the Hull plant in 1986. There are numerous molds manufactured in large quantities.

Row 1
    1. square baking dish...$20
    2. Corky pig bank...$40
    3. small bean pot...$15
    4. bean pot $30

Row 2
    1. hen casserole 11 1/2" x 13 1/2" $65
    2. chip & dip bowl...$20
    3. coffee pot $45
    4. cream pitcher $10

Row 3
    1. cup..$ 5
    2. gingerbread man plate $35
    3. & 4. spoon rests (gift from Crooksville Bank 1982) $20
    5. leaf dish $10

Row 1
1. milk pitcher $35
2. mug $10
3. plate 9 1/2" $10
4. platter...$15
5. salt & pepper - jug shaped pr. $20

Row 2
1. salt & pepper - mushroom shaped pr. $20
2. serving dish...$20
3. soup bowl...$10
4. spoon rest $20
5. sugar bowl..$10

Original label used with the pie pans.

Row 1

This 4 piece train canister set was produced during the final days of the Hull factory. The HULL POTTERY newsletter reports that only a few sets were completed and the train set is bound to be a special item for collectors. Prices are being quoted from $2000 - $3000 a set.

Row 2

Gingerbread men cookie jars shown in 3 colors .....$125 each

The depot cookie jar was designed by Louise Bauer as a companion piece to the train set but was not put into production before the factory closed. In 1992 Larry Taylor, president of the Hull Pottery Company, produced a limited number of these depots valued at $250. The advertising plaque was a souvenir sold at the Ohio ceramic center in 1992.

Often the apple cookie jar, grease jar, and salt and pepper set have been reported as manufactured by Hull.

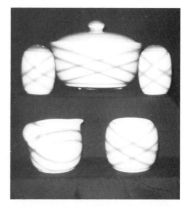

Red plaidware dishes owned by Charles Endres.

Relish plates – $35

Skillet tray – $125

Production of the orchid pitcher was just beginning when the plant closed.

IMPERIAL, NOVELTY, & MISC.

Imperial has been manufactured since the 1960's. The production of Imperial and other miscellaneous patterns is so extensive it is difficult to catalog. The Imperial section will therefore include many miscellaneous items produced not only under the Imperial name but one will also find Athena, Regal, Floraline, Royal, and others. They are pictured in numerical order for the reader's convenience. This section also includes groupings of birds and fowl, animals, Madonnas, and other human figures.

Row 1
1. F1 green fan...$5
2. B2 planter-mushroom design...............................$10
3. F2 goblet planter...$5
4. A3 square planter - leaf design $5
5. F3 goblet planter...$5
6. A4 rectangular planter $10

Row 2
1. 5 Tokay jardiniere $20
2. F5 gold trimmed goblet...$10
3. A6 free form planter $10
4. B6 7" bow...$10
5. F6 pedestal plate..$10

Row 3
1. F8 pedestal bowl...$10
2. F9 oval planter...$5
3. F10 round bowl $5
4. F11 rectangular planter $5

Row 1

1. 14 ribbed planter $5
2. 15 goblet $5
3. F16 free form bowl $15
4. F16 rectangular planter - butterfly design...........$15
5. F17 rectangular planter - floral design................$15
6. F18 rectangular planter - grape design $15

Row 2

1. I18 free form bowl - leaf design $15
2. F19 free form bowl - clover design.......................$15
3. I20 ash tray - heart shape $35
4. I21 oval planter..$10
5. F22 pedestal planter..$10

Row 3

1. F24 basket...$20
2. F25 soap dish $20
3. F26 pitcher - vegetable design..............................$25
4. F27 pedestal planter..$10

Row 1

1. F30 10" Fantasy pedestal vase $15
2. 31 divided leaf candy dish 8 3/4".........................$15
3. B32 oval planter - floral design 7".........................$10
4. F33 goblet with sailing vessel in 23 Karate gold trim $25
5. 34 large leaf shaped bowl.......................................$25

Row 2

1. F38 Rainbow/Capri basket....................................$40
2. 39 13" Fantasy vase $30
3. F39 oval planter...$10
4. B41 9" pedestal vase...$25
5. F41 rectangular planter $10
6. F42 rectangular planter $10

Row 3

1. F45 ribbed goblet..$5
2. F47 window box...$15
3. F48 free form bowl...$15
4. F49 lion head goblet...$25
5. F49 planter with cupid design $25

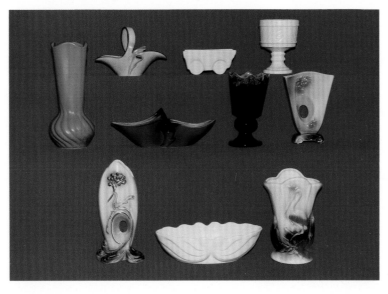

Row 1

1. 56 Parchment & Pine basket $25
2. F56 wheeled white planter....................................$10
3. F63 goblet with leaf design $10

Row 2

1. F70 12" green bulb vase $25
2. 71 Parchment & Pine console bowl $20
3. 72 8" pedestal vase $20
4. 72 8" flowered see-through vase $35

Row 3

1. 73 10" bird see-through vase with gold trim.......$35
2. F77 oval planter...$15
3. 78 9" bird vase..$50

A-50 pitcher – $45.

IMPERIAL, NOVELTY, & MISC.

Row 1

1. 82 12" Fantasy window box....................................$25
2. 83 Mayfair hand vase with 23 Karat gold trim...$35
3. 85 large leaf shaped flat bowl...............................$25
4. 88 console bowl and candleholder (consolette)..$25

Row 2

1. F89 9" square vase..$20
2. 91 console bowl and candleholder (consolette)...$35
3. F91 5" pitcher with eagle design $20
4. 92 7" planter with black flowers............................$50

Row 3

1. 94 large bucket...$75
2. B94 bucket 9"..$45
3. F95 8" round footed bowl.......................................$15
4. F96 rectangular planter $10

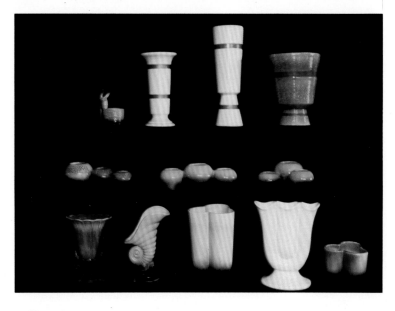

Row 1
1. 101 wishing well planter $15
2. 102 12" gold banded vase....................................$35
3. 104 15" gold banded vase....................................$50
4. 105 8 1/2" gold banded vase $50

Row 2
1. 105 triple bulb planter $25
2. 106 triple bulb planter 10 1/2" $25
3. 107 triple bulb planter $25

Row 3
1. 108 Woodland suspended vase...........................$35
2. 108 Athena shell cornucopia 8 1/2".....................$35
3. 110 9" triple vase..$30
4. 112 10" triple vase..$40
5. 121 5" triple vase..$20

Row 1
1. 150 pedestal planter ....$ 5
2. 151 free form window box $25
3. 152 free form window box $25
4. 153 Fantasy rectangular window box 12 1/2" $30

Row 2
1. 156 pedestal planter $20
2. 157 pedestal rectangular planter...........................$20
3. 158 square candy dish with lid $40
4. 159 pedestal fruit bowl $50

Row 3
1. 161 8" vase $15
2. 162 11" vase $35
3. 163 12" vase $35
4. 201 shell cornucopia $25
5. 203 shell cornucopia $25

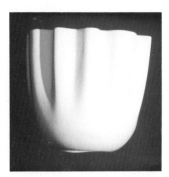

Hull 427 9 1/2 x 10 1/2
large white planter – $75.

Row 1
1. 307 Regal shell cornucopia $25
2. 401 rectangular planter..$10
3. 402 rectangular planter..$25
4. 407 Floraline ribbed goblet $10
5. 415 snail shell cornucopia $35

Row 2
1. 418 5" jardiniere...$15
2. 419 6" jardiniere...$25
3. 450 cart rectangular planter...................................$10
4. F467 ribbed rectangular planter...........................$10
5. F469 ribbed rectangular planter...........................$10

Row 3
1. 491 goblet $10
2. 530 clock planter..$50
3.   conch shell..$35
4.   silver goblet with 4 faces..............................$50
5.   ash tray unicorn design.................................$40

Row 1

1.   cat/kitten lamp $75
2. 61 cat/kitten basket planter $40
3. 89 cat/kitten & spool planter $40
4. 38 dog/poodle hat planter $25
5. 114 poodle base $40
6. 119 15" dog/dachshund planter $75

Row 2

1. 57 9" deer planter $30
2. 62 12" deer planter $45
3. 115 9" giraffe planter $35
4.   horse/colt dish planter $60
5. 965 lamb planter $45

Row 3

1. 39 pig planter $25
2. 196 House & Garden sitting pig $50
3.   Corky pig bank $50
4. 98 10" unicorn vase $35
5. 98 12" unicorn vase $45

Row 1 Male/Female turnabout cat 11" – $75; Cat vase 809 11" – $50.
Row 2 Teddy Bear Planter 811 7" – $35; Siamese cats 63 5 3/4" – $45.

The man on the donkey figurine was made at the Hull Pottery Company and sent to President Franklin D. Roosevelt during WWII. The donkey represents the democratic party. Gladys Showers was the decorator.

The poodle & kitten planters in matte finish are usually found in gloss – $135 each.

The bank on the right is marked hull USA 107 and is much larger than the more common corky pig.

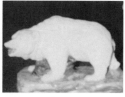

The rabbit candy dish is a Hull experimental piece that never put into full production.

Bear dated 1931 was photographed at the Hull convention at Crooksville, Ohio in 1992.

Little pig banks – $25

Row 1
1. 405 bird $15
2. F473 chickadee $20
3. 53 chicken/rooster $20
4. 95 House & Garden chicken/rooster $40

Row 2
1. 74   bandanna duck $45
2. 75 bandanna duck $30
3. 76 bandanna duck $20
4. 77 bandanna duck candleholder $60
5. 540 flying duck wall planter $95

Row 3
1. 67 flying goose wall planter ..$35
2. 94 twin geese $25
3. 95 twin geese $45
4. 231E goose planter $50
5. 411 long neck goose $50
6. 41 long neck goose $15

Handled gooose basket No. 413
– $75. Penquin planter is F472 –
$25.

Row 1
1. 93 Royal love birds...$40
2. 60 parrot planter..$30
3. 61 pheasant planter..$30

Row 2
1. F23 Capri goose...$50
2. F21 Capri goose...$15
3. 69 goose $40

Row 3
1. 80 goose....................$30
2. goose............................$15
3. 81 double swan $65

This bird flower frog is a rare item in Hull's designs. The bird flower frog 10 1/2" is $75. The 13" low flower bowl base in number 85 for $35.

Flying duck planter number 104 – $85.

Row 1
1. tulip shaped lamp $85
2. 24 Madonna $25
3. 25 Madonna $30

Row 2
1. 26 Madonna $30
2. 27 standing Madonna...$45
3. F61 Madonna $35
4. 81 standing Madonna...$35

Row 3
1. 89 Saint Francis $55
2. 204 Madonna........................$25
3. 417 Madonna........................$50

Coronet Queen with crown
vace #209 - 9" – $50.

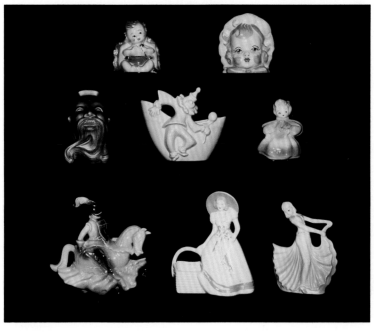

Row 1
1. 92 baby & pillow planter.................................$25
2. 62 child planter..$25

Row 2
1. 120 Chinese man wall planter.............................$25
2. 82 clown planter..$35
3. 90 little girl planter...................................$25

Row 3
1. 55 knight on horse planter...............................$65
2. 954 lady & basket planter................................$40
3. 955 dancing lady planter.................................$50

Band members sell at $100 to $150 each

IRIS/NARCISSUS

The Iris (Narcissus) pattern was produced in as many as four sizes for each mold, making it interesting for the collector to search for each size. Manufactured in the middle 1940's, Iris is found in colors of peach, pink/blue, and shades of rose/peach.

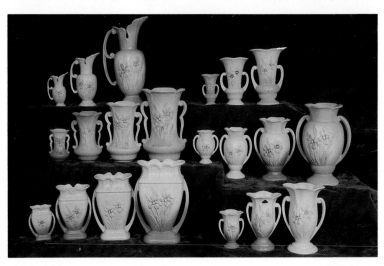

Row 1
1. 401-5" pitcher $75
2. 401-8" pitcher $200
3. 401-13 1/2" pitcher..$450
4. 402-4 3/4" vase $50
5. 402-7" vase..$95
6. 402-8 1/2" vase $125

Row 2
1. 403-4 3/4" vase $50
2. 403-7" vase..$95
3. 403-8 1/2" vase $125
4. 403-10 1/2" vase $300
5. 404-4 3/4" vase $40
6. 404-7" vase..$95
7. 404-8 1/2" vase $125
8. 404-10 1/2" vase $300

Row 3
1. 405-4 3/4" vase $50
2. 405-7" vase..$95
3. 405-8 1/2" vase $125
4. 405-10 1/2" vase $300
5. 406-4 3/4" vase $50
6. 406-7" vase..$95
7. 406-8 1/2" vase $125
NP. 406-10 1/2" vase..$300

Row 1
1. 407-4 3/4" vase $50
2. 407-7" vase...$95
3. 407-8 1/2" vase $125
4. 408-7" basket $275

Row 2
1. 409-12" console bowl..$200
2. 410-7 1/2" bud vase $115
3. 411-5" candleholders pr...$125

Row 3
1. 412-4" hanging basket planter $65
2. 412-7" hanging basket planter $125
3. 413-5 1/2" jardiniere $95
4. 413-9" jardiniere..$300
5. 414-10 1/2" vase $300
6. 414-16" floor vase $500

Hull, it seems, was never in the lamp business, but a number of lamp bases seem to show up and are considered as employee specials made for gifts or their own personal use.

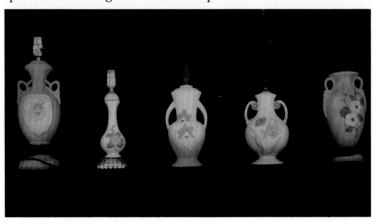

1. lamp base, unnamed design, L-1, 12 3/4" $400
2. lamp base, Classic design, unmarked 7 3/4"..............$150
3. lamp base, Orchid, 317, 10"...................................$500
4. lamp base, unnamed design, 9", USA No. I $500
5. lamp base, Rosella, L-3, 11"...................................$300

Row 1
1. tulip shaped lamp $95
2. kitten planter...$85
3. pheasant planter...$60

Row 2
1. Little Red Riding Hood lamp...............................Rare
2. Rosella lamp 6 3/4"...$225
3. Tulip lamp...$550

Rare Tulip lamp base, 100-3-6 1/2" $500; 107-33-10" $600; 107-33-61/2" $500

Wooldland Candleholder Lamps, pair - $500.

1. Water Lily Lamp - $450. 2. Woddland Teapot Lamp - $500.

A "one of a kind" lamp designed and presented to the original owner. He shared this beautiful lamp with the Hull collectors at the First Annual Hull convention in 1992 in Crooksville, Ohio.

Lovely Magnolia tasseled vase 21" x 12 1/2" lamp - $500.

Pair of Bowknot B-4 lamps - $400 each.

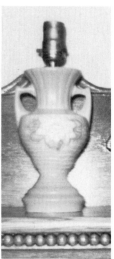

Iris 414 16" - $750

Employee spe-
cialty Waterlily
lamp in a rare
shade of green -
$500

Novelty Lamp - $600

These lamps use the Little Red Riding Hood decal but are
probably not Hull ....$100-$200

The pig and elephant liquor bottles were produced by Hull for the Leeds Company in the middle 1940's. The pig and the elephant are 7 3/4". Prices vary widely on Leeds items. Prices are cheaper near Crooksville, Ohio and surrounding states and appear to be much higher the further away you are. I have been quoted prices from $20 to $165.

Pig banks, 5".

Leeds pig lamp.

LITTLE RED RIDING HOOD

The Little Red Riding Hood items were produced in the late 1950's with several markings. Many are marked Little Red Riding Hood, Pat-Des-No-135889 U.S.A. Others bear the number 967. Blank molds were sold to and decorated by Royal & Regal. Other companies have claimed they produced many of the Little Red Riding Hood items using the poppy decal that Hull used for decorating.

Row 1
    1. advertising plaque ....Rare
    2. baby feeding dish..Rare
    3. baby or chocolate mug ....Rare
    4. wall bank $3000
    5. standing bank $650

Row 2
    1. butter dish $400
    2. cereal canister $1100
    3. coffee canister $650
    4. flour canister $650
    5. popcorn canister $2500

Row 3
    1. potato chip canister...$2500
    2. pretzel canister $2500
    3. sugar canister..$650
    4. salt canister..$1100
    5. Tea canister $650

Row 1
1. small single decal $350
2. large single decal $375
3. two decals $350
4. three decals $350
5. four decals $350

Row 2
1. cold painted (varies by condition of paint) $300-$1000
2. gold star apron/sprig border $500
3. gold star apron/scattered orange flowers..........$400
4. gold star apron/2 spring border........................$400
5. gold star apron/4 decals $400

Row 3
1. gold bowed apron/red shoes & red spray.........$800
2. gold bowed apron/red shoes & red spray.........$800
3. closed basket, two decals $400
4. gold bowed apron, closed basket, 3 decals, red shoes....$500
5. green basket, poinsettia, decals & red shoes ..$900-$1000

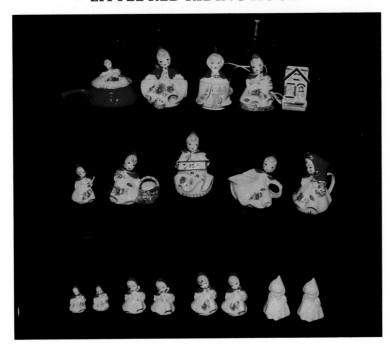

Row 1
1. Little Red Riding Hood covered casserole (very rare)
2. cracker jar $600
3. dresser/grease jar Hull Ware 982 USA..............$600
4. lamp ....Rare
5. match box for wooden matches $800

Row 2
1. 5 1/2" mustard jar with spoon $400
2. planter ....Very rare
3. 9" wall pocket planter..$500
4. 6 1/2" batter pitcher...$425
5. 8" milk pitcher $300

Row 3
1-2. 3 1/2" small salt & pepper shakers $55
3-4. 4 1/2" medium salt & pepper shakers.............$800
5-6. 5 1/2" large salt & pepper shakers $125
7-8. 5 1/2" sitting salt & pepper shakers.................Rare

Row 1
1. stringholder $3000
2. allspice spice jar $700
3. cinnamon spice jar..$700
4. cloves spice jar..$700
5. ginger spice jar $700
6. nutmeg spice jar..$700
7. pepper spice jar $700

Row 2
1. side pour sugar $150
2. side pour creamer...$150
3. crawling sugar..$250
4. tab handle creamer $250
5. sugar with lid $400
6. creamer with pantaloons....................................$400

Row 3
1. teapot...$325
2. wolf grease jar, yellow $900
3. wolf grease jar, red $1000

1. LRRH's basket. 2. Unusually painted blank spice jar. 3 & 4. Rare blue and white small salt & pepper shakers. 5. Unusually painted middle sized salt & pepper shakers. 6. Rare blank sitting shaker. (No head holes.)

Rare sitting salt and pepper shakers, cold painted in blue

Rare pink/blue matte finish dresser/grease jar, No. 982 - $800. Unusual paint such as black or yellow bow $700.

Very early cold painted cookie jar and reproduction cookie jar. Notice the reproduction is slightly smaller.

LRRH's basket is the base of a wolf jar. The lid has the flowers and handle. Very Rare.

Red spray sugar & creamer matches the red spray cookie jar.

Shows the wolf jars with one of the wolves ears up and the other wolf with its ears down.

Tea pot with unusual color & design.

This casserole has a very unusual design.

Little Red Riding Hood Baby Dish ....Rare
Mug ....Rare

LITTLE RED RIDING HOOD

The author introduced two new collectibles this year. She is shown with a LRRH Christmas tree on display at the Stone Church Centennial Museum in Huron, SD.

HULL 13 month First Annual Collectable Calendar, features LRRH on both Decembers. Thirteen full color 8 1/2 x 11 pictures suitable for framing. Limited edition of 1000. $10.95 plus $1.05 S & H.

$12.00 Total

Handpainted LRRH Christmas Balls. Beautifully handpainted in a wide variety of colors, jars decorated with poinsettias, green basket, open baskets, bowed apron, red shoes, one, two, three, or four poppy decals or sprigs, etc. Back reads HULL 1992 LRRH. Limited Edition to 500. $10.95 plus $1.05 S & H.

$12.00 Total

Any two for $23.00 – any six for $60.00

A number of companies other than Hull have produced Little Red Riding Hood items. A number used the poppy decals. Many Little Red Riding Hood lovers are collecting these items along with their Hull pieces. The items featured can be purchased from $25 to $300.

Copyright

Patented June 29, 1943   **Des. 135,889**

UNITED STATES PATENT OFFICE

135,889

DESIGN FOR A COOKIE JAR

Louise Elizabeth Bauer, Zanesville, Ohio, assignor to The A. E. Hull Pottery Company, Incorporated, Crooksville, Ohio, a corporation of Ohio

Application April 12, 1943, Serial No. 109,959

Term of patent 7 years

To all whom it may concern:

Be it known that I, Louise Elizabeth Bauer, a citizen of the United States, residing at Zanesville, in the county of Muskingum and State of Ohio, have invented a new, original, and ornamental Design for a Cookie Jar, of which the following is a specification, reference being had to the accompanying drawing, forming part thereof.

Figure 1 is a front elevational view of a cookie jar showing my new design, and

Figure 2 is a side elevational view thereof.

I claim:

The ornamental design for a cookie jar, as shown.

LOUISE ELIZABETH BAUER.

Lusterware was manufactured in the late 1920's in beautiful shades of pink, lavender, blue, green, and yellow. There are at least thirty-five known molds of vases, jardinieres, etc. in this luster finish.

Row 1
1. flower frog...$50
2. low bowl 8" $85
3. bulb bowl 7 1/2"...$75
4. bulb bowl 9 1/2"...$95
5. console bowl 10" $125

Row 2
1. vase 4" $50
2. vase 8" $75
3. vase 8" $75
4. vase 10" $125
5 & 6. candleholder, each $75

Row 3
1. vase 10" $150
2. vase 10" $125
3. vase 11" $150
4. vase 12" $300
5. vase 13" $250

MAGNOLIA (PINK GLOSS)

This is one of the few glossy patterns produced before the 1950 Hull factory fire. It was made using pink clay and cost more to produce than matte Magnolia pieces. The pink glossy Magnolia was produced in the mid 1950's in shades of pink with darker pink or blue flowers. A few were made in glossy white and trimmed in gold. Gold trimmed pieces usually sell at slightly higher prices.

Row 1

    1. H-1 5 1/2" vase $30

    2. H-2 5 1/2" vase $30

    3. H-3 5 1/2" pitcher $40

Row 2

    1. H-4 6 1/2" vase $30

    2. H-5 6 1/2" vase $30

    3. H-6 6 1/2" vase $30

    4. H-7 6 1/2" vase $30

Row 3

    1. H-8 8 1/2" vase gold trim $65

    2. H-9 8 1/2" vase $65

    3. H-10 8 1/2" cornucopia $65

    4. H-11 8 1/2" pitcher (shown in matte finish)................$75

Row 1
1. H-12 10 1/2" vase $75
2. H-13 10 1/2" vase $75
3. H-14 10 1/2" basket...$225
4. H-15 12" double cornucopia $75

Row 2
1. H-16 12 1/2" winged vase.....................................$150
2. H-17 12 1/2" tassel vase $150
3. H-18 12 1/2" vase $150
4. H-19 13 1/2" pitcher (shown in matte finish)............$250

Row 3
1. H-20 6 1/2" teapot gold trimmed $125
2. H-21 3 3/4" creamer gold trimmed $50
3. H-22 3 3/4" sugar/lid...$50
4. H-23 13" console bowl $75
5. H-24 4" pair of candleholders...............................$75
6. Copy of Hull pottery vase (poor quality)............$10

H-15 12" double cornucopia
with experiemental point.

Salesmen sampler vases with H-12 10 1/2" and H-19 13 1/2" pitcher.

MAGNOLIA (MATTE)

The Magnolia pattern was produced prolifically in the middle 1940's and was a great favorite. Magnolia pieces are one of the most easily found designs in antique shops due to the many pieces produced. Magnolia is found in shades of brown (from yellow to a dusty rose), and in pink/blue shades.

Row 1

1. 1 8 1/2" vase..$95
2. 2 8 1/2" vase..$95
3. 3 8 1/2" vase..$95
4. 4 6 1/2" vase..$45
5. 5 7" pitcher..$95

Row 2

1. 6 12" double cornucopia.......................................$125
2. 7 8 1/2" vase..$95
3. 8 10 1/2" vase..$125
4. 9 10 1/2" vase..$125
5. 10 10 1/2" basket $300

Row 3

1. 11 6 1/2" vase..$45
2. 12 6 1/2" vase..$45
3. 13 4 3/4" vase..$40
4. 14 4 3/4" pitcher $45
5. 15 6 1/2" vase..$45

Row 1
1. 16 15" floor vase..$400
2. 17 12 1/2" winged vase $225
3. 18 13 1/2" pitcher $300

Row 2
1. 19 8" cornucopia (hand painted over matte) $95
2. 20 15" floor vase..$400
3. 21 12 1/2" tassel vase $225
4. 22 12 1/2" vase..$225

Row 3
1. 23 6 1/2" teapot $150
2. 24 3 3/4" creamer $50
3. 25 3 3/4" sugar (no lid)...$50
4. 26 12 1/2" console bowl $150
5. 27 4" candleholders pr. $100

**Rare item marked
Hull Art USA 13-4 3/4**

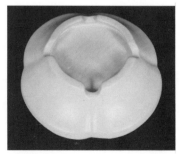

**This ashtray was made from the
base of the 20 - 15" vase.**

MARQUEST

Marquest is kitchen and casual ware manufactured in the 1960's.

Row 1
1-3. nested mixing bowls..............................$15, $25, $35

Row 2
1-4. mugs 3 3/4" $15
5. cocoa pot 11" $65

Lucky collector Doug Burrey owns this lovely 9 1/2" Morning Glory "one of a kind" experimental vase. Doug says it was designed by Warren Garrett at Hull Pottery Factory in 1947.

Don Rowden sent me this picture of his lovely experimental Morning Glory vase for publication in this book.

The oven proof Nuline Bak-Serve kitchenware pieces appeared in the late 1930's in shades of rose, light peach, and blues. The designs were marked by a B for a diamond effect, a C for scales, and a D for a panelled effect. The molds were for bowls, bean pots, pitchers, casseroles and other kitchen items.

Row 1
1. B-6 6 1/2" bowl...$25
2. B-6 8 1/2" bowl...$35
3. B-13 7 1/2" casserole with lid $50

Row 2
1. B-20 cookie jar (no lid)..$50
2. B-29 pitcher $85

Hull manufactured Old Spice mugs for the use of the Shulton Company in the 1930's and 1940's. The glazed mug features the picture of a blue sailing ship with Old Spice written in Red.

Old Spice Mug..$20-40

OPEN ROSE/CAMELLIA

The Open Rose or Camellia pattern is one of the most prolific in the Hull matte finish patterns. The Open Rose or Camellia design on pink/cream/blue, white, or cream background is truly a beautiful pattern.

Row 1

1. 101 8 1/2" cornucopia..$110
2. 102 8 1/2" vase...$125
3. 103 8 1/2" vase...$110
4. 104 10 1/2" mermaid planter..............................Rare
5. 105 7" pitcher..$195

Row 2

1. 106 13 1/2" pitcher $550
2. 107 6" basket...$275
3. 108 8 1/2" vase...$175
NP. 109 (Suspended vase) ....Rare
4. 110 8 1/2" teapot $325
5. 111 5" creamer..$85
6. 112 5" sugar...$85

Row 3

1. 113 7" bowl...$95
2. 114 8 1/2" jardiniere with rams head handles ..$350
3. 115 8 1/2" pitcher...$225
4. 116 12" console bowl..$275
5-6. 117 6 1/2" dove candleholders pr....................$250

Row 1

1. 118 6 1/2" swan vase $110
2. 119 8 1/2" vase...$110
3. 120 6 1/4" vase...$85
4. 121 6 1/4" vase...$85

Row 2

1. 122 6 1/4" vase...$85
2. 123 6 1/2" vase...$85
3. 124 12" vase $275
4. 125 8 1/2" wall pocket $275

Row 3

1. 126 8 1/2" hand vase..$225
2. 127 4 3/4" vase...$45
3. 128 4 3/4" pitcher $65
4. 129 7" bud vase $95

Row 1

1. 130 4 3/4" vase..$55
2. 131 4 3/4" vase..$55
3. 132 7" hanging basket..$200
4. 133 6 1/4" vase..$85
5. 134 6 1/4" vase..$85

Row 2

1. 135 6 1/4" vase..$85
2. 136 6 1/4" vase..$85
3. 137 6 1/4" vase..$85
4. 138 6 1/4" vase..$85

Row 3

1. 139 10 1/2" lamp vase...$400
2. 140 10 1/2" basket..$800-$1000
3. 141 8 1/2" cornucopia..$135
4. 142 6 1/4" basket..$300
5. 143 8 1/2" vase..$150

104 10 1/2" mermaid planter.

This is a very rare (possibly one of a kind) open rose coffee pot.

The flowers on this Open Rose 102-8 1/2 vase are brightly painted with orange flowers and trimmed in gold.

ORCHID

Orchid, a lovely matte finish pottery manufactured in the late 1930's, was produced in more than one size in many of the molds. Colors are shades of pink/blue, cream/blue, and pink/cream.

Row 1
NP. 300 6 1/2" vase $125
1. 301 4 3/4" vase...$75
2. 301 6" vase $125
3. 301 8 1/2" vase...$175
4. 301 10" vase $300

Row 2
1. 302 4 3/4" vase...$75
2. 302 6" vase $125
3. 302 8" vase $175
4. 302 10" vase $300

Row 3
1. 303 4 3/4" vase $75
2. 303 6" vase......................$125
3. 303 8" vase......................$175
4. 303 10" vase.....................$300
NP. 304 4 1/2" vase..............$75
5. 304 6" vase......................$125
6. 304 8 1/2" vase $175
7. 304 10 1/4 vase...............$300

Experiemental vase using the orchid 303 4 3/4" mold - $75.

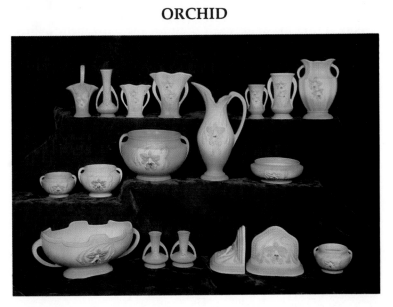

Row 1

1. 305 7" basket..$500
2. 306 6 3/4" bud base......................................$125
3. 307 4 3/4" vase...$75
4. 307 6 1/2" vase...$125
NP. 307 8" vase $175
NP. 307 10" vase $300
5. 308 4 3/4" vase...$75
6. 308 6 1/2" vase...$125
NP. 308 8" vase $175
NP. 308 10" vase $300
7. 309 8 1/2" vase...$175

Row 2

1. 310 4 3/4" jardiniere...$95
2. 310 6" jardiniere $175
3. 310 9 1/2" jardiniere.......................................$400
4. 311 13" pitcher...$600
5. 312 7" bowl..$100

Row 3

1. 314 13" console bowl......................................$300
2. 315 4" candleholders pr. $200
3 & 4. 316 7" bookends ....$800-$1200
5. 317 4 3/4" jardiniere...$75

(*NP - not pictured)

PARCHMENT & PINE

Pine sprays make up the design for the Parchment & Pine pottery manufactured in the early 1950's in high gloss shades of green and brown.

Row 1
1. S-1 5" vase...$50
2. S-2 R 8" cornucopia $50
3. S-2 L 8" cornucopia $50
4. S-3 6" basket $75
5. S-4 10" vase..$75
6. S-5 10 1/2" window box...$85

Row 2
1. S-6 L 12" cornucopia $90
2. S-6 R 12" cornucopia $90
3. S-7 13 1/2" pitcher...$185
4. S-8 16" basket $160
5. S-9 16" console bowl.................$95

Row 3
1. S-10 2 1/4" candleholders pr....$50
2. S-11 6" teapot............................$100
3. S-12 3 1/4" creamer $35
4. S-13 3 1/4" sugar with lid.........$35
5. S-14 14" ash tray.......................$110
6. S-15 8" coffee pot......................$125

PAGODA

Twelve molds were used in manufacturing the Pagoda pattern in 1960. They include vases & planters in shades of orange, green & white. Prices range from $10 to $40.

P5-12 1/2" vase

The very beautiful Pine Cone pattern was manufactured in the late 1930's in only one mold, however it does come in several shades of pinks, blues, and turquoise. $150.

Parchment & Pine tea set in it's original box used for display in stores.

Poppy flowers decorate this mold manufactured in the 1940's in lovely shades of pink/blue, cream and pink/cream. This pattern features more than one size in several of the molds.

Row 1

    1. 601 9" basket ....$400-$600
    2. 601 12" basket ....$1000-$1200
    3. 602 6 1/2" planter $150

Row 2

    1. 603 4 3/4" jardiniere..............................$65
    2. 604 8" cornucopia $225
    NP. 605 4 3/4" vase...................................$65
    NP. 605 6 1/2" vase...................................$95
    3. 605 8 1/2" vase.....................................$150
    NP. 605 10 1/2" vase.................................$300
    NP. 606 4 3/8" vase...................................$65
    4. 606 6 1/2" vase.....................................$95
    5. 606 8 1/2" vase.....................................$150
    6. 606 10 1/2" vase...................................$300

Row 3

    1. 607 4 3/4" vase.....................................$65
    2. 607 6 1/2" vase.....................................$95
    3. 607 8 1/2" vase.....................................$150
    4. 607 10 1/2" vase...................................$300

Row 1

1. 608 4 3/4" jardiniere..$75
2. 609 9" wall planter..$350

Row 2

1. 610 4 3/4" pitcher $100
2. 610 13" pitcher ....$500-$700
NP. 611 4 3/4" vase..$65
3. 611 6 1/2" vase..$95
NP. 611 8 1/2" vase..$150
NP. 611 10 1/2" vase..$300
NP. 612 4 3/4" vase..$65
4. 612 6 1/2" vase..$95
NP. 612 8" vase $150
NP. 612 10 1/2" vase..$300

Brown, butterscotch, green and tangerine are the four colors for Rainbow in Hull's House & Garden pattern. The pattern features the foam edge and was manufactured in the 1960's. The Rainbow line includes casual dinnerware as well as mixing bowls and serving pieces.

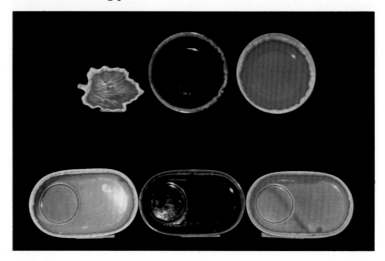

Row 1
  1. leaf dish $10
  2-3. salad plates $10

Row 2
  1-3. soup & sandwich trays $15

Rosella window box ....Rare

Rosella is one of the few high gloss Hull patterns manufactured before 1950. It was manufactured in the late 1940's in shades of pink and ivory.

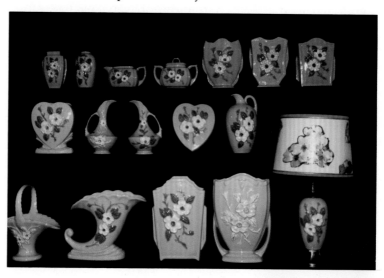

Row 1

1. R-1 5" vase $35
2. R-2 5" vase $35
3. R-3 5 1/2" creamer $50
4. R-4 5 1/2" sugar/lid..................$60
5. R-5 6 1/2" vase...........................$45
6. R-6 6 1/2" vase...........................$45
7. R-7 6 1/2" vase...........................$45

Row 2

1. R-8 6 1/2" vase...........................$75
2. R-9 6 1/2" L pitcher....................$75
3. R-9 6 1/2" R pitcher....................$75
4. R-10 61/2" hanging planter $85
5. R-11 7" R pitcher.........................$85

Row 3

1. R-12 7" basket...........................$185
2. R-13 8 1/2" L cornucopia...........$75
3. R-14 8 1/2" vase..........................$75
4. R-15 8 1/2" vase..........................$75
5. 6 3/4" lamp.................................$250
Page 90 window box.....................Rare

R-1 5" vase shown in rare matte pink/blue colors.

This R-7 9 1/2" pitcher is rare.

ROYAL

The Royal pottery was made in the 1950's after the factory fire. It is in high gloss pink or turquoise with a spattered effect and black shading. Woodland, Ebb Tide, Imperial, and other mold shapes were used in the manufacturing of many Royal pieces.

Row 1
1. E1 6 1/2" Ebb Tide fish vase $35
2. W4 6 1/2" Woodland vase $35
3. W6 6 1/2" Woodland pitcher $45
4. W8 7 1/2" Woodland vase $40
5. W9 8 3/4" Woodland basket $50
6. W10 11" Woodland Cornucopia $45

Row 2
1. W13 7 1/2" Woodland shell wall planter $50
2. W22 10 1/2" Woodland basket $135
3. W26 Woodland teapot..$95
4. W28 Woodland creamer $25
5. W29 13" Woodland console bowl $75
6. W30 Woodland candleholder...............................$25

Row 3
1. 65 6" pedestal planter $25
2. 75 6" jardiniere..$35
3. -4. 86 & 87 Butterfly lavo bowl set......................$100
5. 91 pigeon planter...$30
6. 93 love birds..$30

Unknown pattern marked D-4-6 1/2" owned by Gayle McGooden.

These 3 1/2" tumblers were used to experiment on paint colors and finishes before putting new designs into production. – $10.

Miniature replicas are often carried by salesmen. These miniatures of Hull are owned by Duke Frash.

The experimental Jonquil/ Daffodil and the Iris vase are owned by Joan Hull

The Little Texan Bank was made for Graham Chevrolet of Mansfield, Ohio in 1972 as a promotional item for Mr. Graham's car dealership. These banks were handpainted by Gladys Showers in her home. Gladys is the widow of Harold Showers who was the plant manager of the Hull Pottery Company more than 40 years. She was the plants nurse for over 10 years. The bank reads "The Little Texan Save at Graham Chevytown, Mansfield, Ohio."

This 16" reclining Indian is displayed at the Ohio ceramic center. Designed for a client in the late 1930's, it proved too expensive and was not put into production.

The Star Flower vase came from the mold room after the flood and fire at the Hull Pottery Company in 1950. Loads of pottery were hauled to the dump. This vase was later rescued from the dump.

The first and third vases are from the woodland line but with experimental paint. The center vase is Classic.

This beautiful lamp with a design of several flowers is a one of a kind. It was presented to the original owner as a gift many years ago. He was kind enough to share it with the collectors at the Hull Pottery convention in Crooksville, Ohio in 1992.

An experimental wheat vase is in shades of pink & bluegreen.

Double cornucopia in shades of pink & blue.

Cornucopia using a Dogwood flower design.

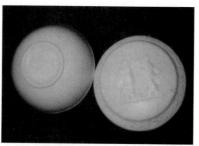

This blue powder jar is incised with the word HULL on the bottom.

SERENADE

The Serenade pattern featuring beautiful birds was manufactured in the late 1950's. Serenade pieces come in shades of light yellow, blue, and pink. Serenade has became one of the fastest selling of the Post 1950 patterns.

Row 1
1. S1 6" vase...$50
2. S2 6" pitcher $60
3. S3 5 3/4" pedestal planter...$50
4. S3C 8 1/4" candy dish with lid $95
5. S4 5" hat shaped vase $55
6. S5 6 3/4" basket...$95

Row 2
1. S6 8 1/2" vase $55
2. S7 8 1/2" vase $55
3. S8 8 1/2" pitcher..$85
4. S9 12 1/2" window box $95
5. S10 11" cornucopia $95
6. S11 10 1/2" vase $95

Row 3
1. S12 14" vase $100
2. S13 13 1/2" pitcher $350
3. S14 12" basket............................$350
4. S15 11 1/2" footed fruit bowl...$110
5. S16 6 1/2" candleholders pr. $70

Row 4
1. S17 6 cup teapot $175
2. S18 3 1/2" creamer.......................$45
3. S19 3 1/2" sugar with lid $45
4. S20 9" covered casserole $125
5. S21 1 1/2 qt. pitcher $125
6. S22 8 oz. mug $55
7. S23 13 x 10 1/2" ash tray.............$95

Beautiful S-14 basket heavily trimmed in gold.

The Stoneware pieces of Hull manufactured in the 1920's came in a multitude of colors, molds, sizes and shapes in both the matte and gloss finish. These pieces are marked with an H enclosed in a circle or a diamond. See Page 6, No. 1.

Row 1
1. 25 Ⓗ vase 5 1/2"...$55
2. 26 Ⓗ vase 8"...$70
3. 32 Ⓗ vase 8"...$70
4. 32 Ⓗ vase 8"...$70
5. 40 Ⓗ vase 7"...$65
6. 39 Ⓗ vase 8"...$70

Row 2
1. 536 Ⓗ jardiniere 5"..$55
2. 536 Ⓗ jardiniere 8"..$85
3. 536 Ⓗ jardiniere 9"..$100
4. 546 Ⓗ jardiniere 3"..$35
5. 546 Ⓗ jardiniere 4"..$35
6. 546 Ⓗ jardiniere 7"..$80

Row 3
1. 550 Ⓗ jardiniere 7"..$85
2. 551 Ⓗ jardiniere 7"..$85
3. Vase, unmarked 7"...$50
4. Hanging basket, unmarked 5"...$80
5. Hanging basket, unmarked 5" $50
6. Flower pot with saucer, unmarked 6" $50

1. Arrowhead design, unmarked - $75
2. Hanging Planter 546 H 4 1/2" x 6" - $95

Stoneware Teapot 6 1/2" - $135

Row 1
1. Ⓗ jardiniere 5 1/2"..$125
2. Ⓗ vase 4 1/2"...$50
3. Ⓗ vase 4 1/2"...$50
4. Ⓗ vase 4 1/2"...$50
5. Ⓗ jardiniere 5 1/4"..$125

Row 2
1. Ⓗ flower pot 6"...$60
2. Ⓗ flower pot 6"...$60
3. Ⓗ flower pot 6"...$60

Row 3
1. Ⓗ bowl 3" $75
2. Ⓗ flower pot 4"...$40
3. Ⓗ flower pot 3 3/4" $35
4. Ⓗ flower pot 4"...$40
5. Ⓗ vase 5 1/2"...$55

Row 1
1. 492 Ⓗ stein 6 1/2" $40
2. 495 Ⓗ flying Order of the Eagles stein...................$70
3. 492 Ⓗ covered pretzel jar 9 1/2" $250
4. 492 Ⓗ tankard 9 1/2" $225
5. 496 Ⓗ Elk stein 6 1/2"...$70
6. American Legion stein 6 1/2"...................................$70

Row 2
1. 491 Ⓗ mug 4 3/4"...$45
2. 493 Ⓗ mug 4 1/4"...$45
3. 493 Ⓗ mug 4 1/4"...$45
4. 494 Ⓗ mug 4 1/2"...$35
5. 497 Ⓗ "Happy Days Are Here Again" mug 4 3/4" $45
6. 497 Ⓗ "Happy Days Are Here Again" mug 4 3/4".....$45

Some harder to find Stoneware pieces are the flowered Ⓗ 6", $95; Tassel 4 3/4", $50 and the Ivy 7 1/2", $95, planters.

Rare handled vase, unmarked 6 1/2" - $95.

STONEWARE

Row 1

1. H coffee canister 6 1/2" $80
2. H sugar canister 6 1/2".............................$80
3. H tea canister 6 1/2" $80
4. H rice canister 6 1/2" $80

Row 2

1. H semi-porcelain pitcher 4 1/4"............................$60
2. H spice jar 3 1/2"............................$65
3. H pepper jar 3 1/2"............................$65
4. H nutmeg jar 3 1/2"............................$65
5. H mustard jar 3 1/2"............................$65
6. H spice jar 3 1/2"............................$65
7. H ginger jar 3 1/2" $65
8. H semi-porcelain pitcher 6 3/4"............................$95

Row 3

1. H vase 6".................................$65
2. 421 H bowl 5"............................$30
3. 160 H custard 2 1/2" $20
4. H bowl 10 1/2" $85
5. 421 H bowl 5"............................$30
6. H bean pot with lid 5" $65

Row 1
1. 100 Ⓗ covered bowl 5 1/2".....................................$60
2. 100 Ⓗ bowl 4"...$25
3. 100 Ⓗ bowl 5"...$30
4. 100 Ⓗ bowl 7"...$40
5. 100 Ⓗ bowl 8"...$50
6. 100 Ⓗ bowl 9"...$60
7. 100 Ⓗ bowl 12"...$80

Row 2
1. 106 Ⓗ handled bake dish 4"..................................$35
2. 106 Ⓗ bake dish 4"..$25
3. 106 Ⓗ bake dish 6"..$35
4. 106 Ⓗ bake dish 8"..$45
5. 106 Ⓗ bake dish 9"..$50

Row 3
1. 106 Ⓗ jug..$55
2. 106 Ⓗ jug..$65
3. 111 Ⓗ salt box 6"..$125
4. 114 Ⓗ custard cup 2"..$25
5. 114 Ⓗ custard cup 2"..$25
6. 113 Ⓗ covered casserole 7 1/2"..............................$65

SUN GLOW

Sun Glow pottery is a glossy pink or yellow pansy and butterfly design manufactured in the early 1950's for ten cent store distribution.

Row 1
1. Bell $75
2. Bell (Loop or Needle Handle) $75
3. 83 Iron Wall Pocket...$65
4. 50-5 1/2" Bowl...$20
5. 50- 7 1/2" Bowl..$30
6. 50 - 9 1/2" Bowl...$40
7. 51 7 1/2" Covered Casserole $50

Row 2
1. 52 24 oz. Pitcher...$35
2. 53 Grease Jar $35
3. 54 Salt & Pepper Shakers $20
4. 55 7 1/2" Beverage Pitcher..$85
5. 80 Cup/Saucer/Wall Pocket.....................................$65
6. 81 Pitcher/Wall Pocket $65
7. 82 Whisk Broom;/Wall Pocket $65

Row 3
1. 84 6 1/2" Basket..$65
2. 85 8 3/4" Bird Vase $45
3. 88 5 1/2" Vase...$35
4. 89 5 1/2" Vase...$35
5. 90 6 1/2" Pitcher...$40
6. 91 6 1/2" Vase...$40
7. 92 6 1/2" Vase...$40
8. 93 6 1/2" Vase...$40

Row 4
1. 94 8" Vase $45
2. 95 8 1/2" Vase...$45
3. 96 8 1/2" Cornucopia $50
4. 97 5 1/2" Flower Pot...$35
5. 98 7 1/2" Flower Pot...$45
6. 99 6" Hanging Basket...$65
7. 100 6 1/2" Vase...$40

Made in 1960 these Supreme items are considered experimental as they were never sold on the market. Colors are shades of green and brown & orange.

Row 1
1. urn 6"...$100
2. urn 4 1/2"...$100
3. bowl 4 1/4"...$100

Row 2
1. candy dish 7"..$125
2. basket 8 1/2" $125
3. vase 8" $75

Row 3
1. vase 12 1/2"...$175
2. pitcher 10"...$200
3. pedestal vase 10" $150
4. lamp 12 1/2" $200

Only four molds were used to make the Thistle pattern in the late 1930's in colors of pink, blue, or turquoise. Numbered 51, 52, 53, 54, all are 6 1'2" - $125-$150.

Wall and floor tiles were manufactured by Hull in the late 1920's and into the 1930's in a large variety of colors in both matte and gloss finishes. The tiles are 4 1/4" x 4 1/4". The border tile is 2 7/8" x 6". Most of the tiles pictured were purchased in Crooksville, Ohio. They range in price from $25-$300. The tile marked "Pottery Lover's Reunion 1985" was a souvenir gift at that festival.

These nine-tiles are deep black/brown with gold in three dimensional patterns.

Back side of tile marked: Hull - CUSHION TILE.

This window grouping of over 100 tiles was used on the wall behind a soda fountain in a Milwaukee drugstore until 1950 and has been in storage since. The tiles are marked HULL Faience. Faience tiles have unglazed edges usually for cement and grout installation.

The blue and white ship and the pink and blue Fleur-de-lis tiles are marked Hull Faience.

The colors in these tiles are beautiful. The tiles on the border are brown/black showing lots of gold. The tiny border tiles with a rolling pin design and the tiles with designs are three dimensional and created by the squeeze-bag process. This grouping is extremely beautiful and a rare find.

TOKAY/TUSCANY

Tokay/Tuscany is a high gloss pottery with grape and leaf designs. It was manufactured in the late 1950's in white/dark green and shades of green/pink.

Row 1

1. 1 6 1/2" cornucopia...$35
2. 2 6" vase...$35
3. 3 8" pitcher $80
4. 4 8 1/4" vase...$75
5. 5 5 1/2" jardiniere $55
6. 6 8" basket $75
7. 7 9 1/2" fruit bowl..$125
8. 8 10" vase...$95

Row 2

1. 9 compote $50
2. 9c 8 1/2" candy dish $95
3. 10 11" cornucopia $55
4. 11 10 1/2" moon basket.........$95
5. 12 12" vase $85
6. 13 12" pitcher........................$175

Row 3

1. 14 15 3/4" consolette............$145
2. 15 12" basket.........................$175
3. 16 teapot $125
4. 17 creamer $35
5. 18 sugar with lid...................$35
6. 19 leaf dish $55
7. 21 14" pitcher.......................$175

This hard to find Tokay number 20 is 15" tall - $200.

There are only seven known, highly sought after Tropicana molds. Made in the late 1950's, Tropicana is a glossy white featuring Caribbean people.

Row 1

1. T51 5 1/2" flower dish...$350
2. T52 10" x 7 1/2" ashtray $350
3. T53 8 1/2" vase $350

Row 2

1. T54 12 1/2" vase...............................$450
2. T55 12 3/4" basket $650
3. T56 13 1/2" pitcher $550
4. T57 14 1/2" hanging planter vase.$550

This Tropicana basket has a rough texture and is painted yellow much like the Serenade pieces. This possible "one-of-a-kind" basket is owned by Steve Johnson.

A pinecone design was painted on this number T54 12 1/2" vase.

TULIP (SUENO)

The Tulip design vases appeared in the late thirties in shades of pink/blue and cream/blue. Some molds are offered in a variety of sizes.

Row 1

1. 100-33-4" vase $65
2. 100-33-6 1/2" vase $95
3. 100-33-8" vase $150
4. 100-33-10" vase $250

Row 2

NP. 101-33-6 1/2" vase $95
1. 101-33-9" vase $175
NP. 101-33-10" vase $300
2. 102-33-6" basket $225
3. 103-33-6" suspended vase $175

Row 3

1. 104-44-6" bud vase $95
2. 105-33-8" vase $150
3. 106-33-6 1/2" vase $95
4. 107-33-6" vase $95
NP. 107-33-8" vase $150
NP. 107-33-8" lamp (see Page 58) $550

Row 1

1. 108-33-6" vase $95
2. 109-33-8" pitcher..$195
3. 109-33-13" pitcher..$375

Row 2

1. 110-33-6" vase $95
2. 111-33-6" vase $95
3. 115-33-7" large jardiniere $300

Row 3

1. 116-33-4 3/4" flower pot with attached saucer $95
NP. 116-33-6" flower pot with attached saucer......$165
2. 117-30-5" jardiniere $95
4. lamp (same mold as 115-7")..$500

WATER LILY

Water Lily was manufactured in the late 1940's with the water lily flower on water markings. Water Lily is found in shades of tan/brown or pink/turquoise. A few pieces were manufactured in a glossy white with gold trim. Items trimmed in gold are usually slightly higher in price.

Row 1
1. L-A- 8 1/2" vase..$150
2. L-1-5 1/2" vase..$45
3. L-2-5 1/2" vase..$45
4. L-3-5 1/2" pitcher $55
5. L-4-6 1/2" vase..$55
6. L-5-6 1/2" vase..$55

Row 2
1. L-6-6 1/2" vase.............................$55
2. L-7-6 1/2" cornucopia.................$70
3. L-8-8 1/2" vase...........................$125
4. L-9-8 1/2" vase...........................$125
5. L-10-9 1/2" vase.........................$125

Row 3
1. L-11-9 1/2" vase.........................$125
2. L-12-10 1/2" vase.......................$165
3. L-13-10 1/2" vase.......................$165
4. L-14-10 1/2" basket $300

The L-18-6" teapot has a rare ivory & apple green matte finish.

Water Lily's L-17 13 1/2" pitcher painted in yellow with a pink flower.

Row 1
1. L-15-12 1/2" vase..$300
2. L-16-12 1/2" vase..$300
3. L-17-12 1/2" pitcher $350

Row 2
1. L-18-6" teapot...$175
2. L-19-5" creamer..$50
3. L-20-5" sugar with lid $50
4. L-21-13 1/2" console bowl $150
5. L-22-4" candleholders pr. $100

Row 3
1. L-23-5 1/2" jardiniere $95
2. L-24-8 1/2" large jardiniere.....................................$250
3. L-25-5 1/4" planter with attached saucer $125
4. L-27-12" double cornucopia...................................$165

(See Page 60 for lamps)

WILDFLOWER

One of Hull's most popular designs is the Wildflower pattern featuring the three petaled Trillium flower making it easy to identify. It was manufactured in the 1940's, beginning with the numbered series from 51 to 79. The later series is numbered with a W from 1 to 21. Colors are in shades of tan/brown and pink/blue.

Row 1

    1. W-1-5 1/2" vase...$45

    2. W-2-5 1/2" pitcher $65

    3. W-3-5 1/2" vase...$45

    4. W-4-6 1/2" vase...$65

    5. W-5-6 1/2" vase...$65

Row 2

    1. W-6-7 1/2" vase...$75

    2. W-7-7 1/2" cornucopia $75

    3. W-8-7 1/2" vase...$75

    4. W-9-8 1/2" vase...$125

    5. W-10-8 1/2" cornucopia $95

Row 3

    1. W-11-8 1/2" pitcher $150

    2. W-12- 9 1/2" vase...$135

    3. W-13-9 1/2" vase...$135

    4. W-14-10 1/2" vase...$150

Row 1

1. W-15-10 1/2" fan vase $150
2. W-16-10 1/2" basket..$350

Row 2

1. W-17-12 1/4" vase...$200
2. W-18-12 1/2" vase...$200
3. W-19-13 1/2" pitcher $450

Row 3

1. W-20-15" floor vase..$425
2. W-21-12" console bowl $125
3. candleholders pr...$100

Row 1

1. 51 8 1/2" vase...$250
2. 52 5 1/2" vase...$125
3. 53 8 1/2" vase...$250
4. 54 6 1/2" vase...$125

Row 2

1. 55 13 1/2" pitcher.......................................$700-$1000
2. 56 4 1/2" vase..$95
3. 57 4 1/2" pitcher $95
4. 58 6 1/2" cornucopia..$125
5. 59 10 1/2" vase...$250

Row 3

1. 60 6 1/2" vase...$135
2. 61 6 1/2" vase...$135
3. 62 6 1/2" vase...$135
4. 63 7 1/2" pitcher $300
5. 64 4" jardiniere..$75
6. 65 7" low basket...$400-$700

Row 1

1. 64 4" jardiniere $75
2. 65 7" low basket..$400-700
3. 66 10 1/2" basket...$1200-1500
4. 67 8 1/2" vase..$275
5. 68 7 1/2" cornucopia..$115

Row 2

1 & 3. 69 4" candleholders pr. $200
2. 70 12" console bowl....................................$325
4. 71 12" vase $300
5. 72 8" teapot...$700-$1000
6. 73 4 3/4" creamer $250
7. 74 4 3/4" sugar...$250

Row 3

1. 75 8 1/2" vase..$275
2. 76 8 1/2" vase..$275
3. 77 10 1/2" vase...$300
4. 78 8 1/2" vase..$275
5. 79 10 1/2" basket.......................................$1500-$2000

Some Hull Pottery was sold to other companies who painted and sold them under their own company's sticker. These Wildflower items are gold and brown with bright orange and blue flowers.

The rare candleabra in the middle was rescued from the dump after the Crooksville flood and the Hull Pottery Company fire in 1950.

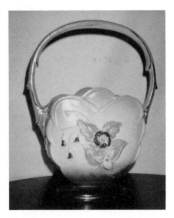

A rare 79 10 1/2" basket and a 61 6 1/4" vase in the bright hand painted colors.

The Woodland pieces were manufactured in three different finishes during the late 1940's and early 1950's. The oldest molds feature a yellow center in the flower and come in shades of cream, rose, and green. Those manufactured after the 1950 factory fire in the matte finish are not as durable as the earlier pieces. These items come in rose, yellow, and green. The newest molds were painted a very high gloss in two-tone shades featuring chartreuse, dark green, blue, rose, and white.

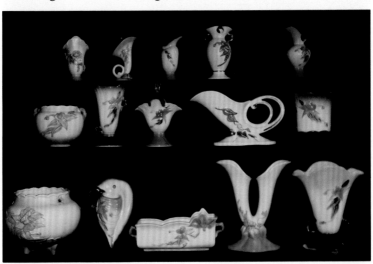

Row 1	Pre 1950	Post 1950	Glossy
1. W1 5 1/2" vase	$55		$35
2. W2 5 1/2" cornucopia	$55	$45	$40
3. W3 5 1/2" pitcher	$65	$50	$45
4. W4 6 1/2" vase	$65	$50	$45
Page 119. W5 6 1/2" cornucopia	$65		
5. W6 6 1/4" pitcher	$85	$75	$65
Row 2			
1. W7 5 1/4" jardiniere	$125	$75	$65
2. W8 7 1/4" vase	$95	$65	$60
3. W9 8 3/4" basket	$185	$125	$110
4. W10 11" cornucopia	$130	$75	$65
(shown in glossy white with gold trim)			
5. W11 5 1/2" flower pot with attached saucer	$150	$100	$75
Row 3			
1. W12 7 1/2" hanging basket	$500		
2. W13 7 1/2" shell wall pocket	$150	$100	$75
3. W14 10" window box	$100	$100	$55
4. W15 8 1/2" double vase	$125	$125	$65
5. W16 8 1/2" vase	$125	$100	$80

WOODLAND

Row 1

		Pre 1950	Post 1950	Glossy
1.	W17 7 1/2" suspended vase	$225		
2.	W18 10 1/2" vase	$165	$125	$95
3.	W19 10 1/2" window box	$125		$95
4.	W21 9 1/2" jardiniere	$650	$500	$250

Row 2

1.	W22 10 1/2" basket	$750	$350	$215
2.	W23 14" double cornucopia	$450		
3.	W24 13 1/2" pitcher	$550	$250	$200
4.	W25 12 1/2" vase	$350		

Row 3

1.	W26 6 1/2" teapot	$325	$175	$125
2.	W27 4 1/2" creamer	$75	$50	$35
3.	W28 3 1/2" sugar with lid	$75	$50	$35
4.	W29 14" console bowl	$275	$175	$100
5.	W30 3 1/2" candleholder ea.	$65	$50	$35
6.	W31 5 1/2" hanging basket	$125		

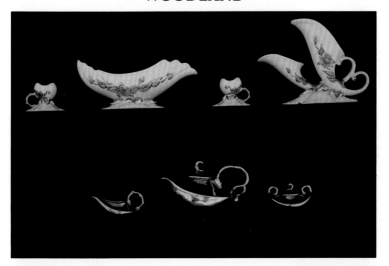

This picture shows a few pieces of Woodland that were manufactured in high gloss white and trimmed in gold. Because of the gold trim, these pieces usually command a slightly higher price than the regular matte molds. Row 2. Woodland gold leaf tea set. Mrs. Gladys Showers, Crooksville, applied the gold to the Hull Pottery tea set and fired it. The set was for Betty and Jackie Grosses' wedding present on June 14, 1962.

This beautiful white glossy set is heavily trimmed in gold.

Experimental W1 5 1/2" and W5 6 1/2" cornucopia

ZANE GREY

Produced in the late 1920's, Zane Grey is a blue banded white kitchenware product. The molds include mixing bowls, pitcher, covered jar, jugs, and other items. The covered jars sell for as high as $300, bowls from $20 to $75, jugs from $25 to $100, and other items selling at similar prices of $10 to $100 and up.

Old advertising photos taken from Better Homes & Gardens Magazines framed by Shari Potmesil.

After the close of the Hull Pottery Company in 1986, they gave some of their inventory to the Ohio Ceramic Center i n Roseville, Ohio.

Nancy Dennis hand painted some of the dinnerware items and they were sold at the Center.

HISTORY
By Dee Konyha

The A.E. Hull Pottery Company was founded in 1905 by Addis Emmet Hull, William Watts, and J.D. Young in Crooksville, Ohio. The Company's production focused on stoneware. In 1907 the Acme Pottery Company, a producer of semi-porcelain dinnerware, was purchased by a brother, an incorporator of the company, who also served as President of the Board of Directors.

After World War I, the company manufactured toilet, kitchen, and lusterware in addition to a line of stoneware items. From 1921 to the Stock Market Crash of 1929, earthenware china and pottery items from Europe were also imported by the Hull company and sold as imported items for less than their own production costs. In 1927 one plant was converted to tiling operations. Three types of tiles were produced: matte, gloss or stipled finishes. Accessory items were also available in matching colors. By 1933 the price of tiles were less than the production costs, and they were discontinued.

When Addis E. Hull, Sr., died in 1930, the oldest son, Addis E. Hull, Jr., took over the company and production continued to consist of lines of stoneware, kitchenware, gardenware, and floristware. In 1937 A.E. Hull, Jr., left the company to manage the Shawnee Pottery Company of Zanesville, Ohio. Gerald F. Watts, son of William Watts, became President of the company. Also in 1937, the company contracted with Shulton of New York for the manufacture of shaving mugs, after shave lotion, cologne and after shave talc bottles. This production continued until 1944. In the late 30's (1938), the first art pottery lines were introduced, which included the Tulip, Calla Lily, Thistle, Pinecone, and Orchid patterns.

During the forties, the matte art pottery lines flourished at the A.E. Hull Pottery Company. These art lines included Iris, Dogwood, Poppy, Open Rose, Magnolia, Wildflower, Wildflower (Number Series), Water Lily, Granada/Mardi Gras, Bow Knot, and Woodland. Many of these pieces have the marks of the decorator on the bottom. Each decorator had a number and/or letter. Two high gloss lines were also produced during this time - Rosella and Magnolia. Rosella was only offered during 1946 because of high costs involved in producing the pink base clay at the factory.

In addition to the art pottery being produced at this time, kitchenware items continued, plus novelty items were introduced in the early 1940's. The year 1943 was highlighted by the introduction of the Red Riding Hood cookie jar, which was patented June 29, 1943 by Louise E. Bauer of Zanesville, Ohio. She assigned her rights to the patent design to the A.E. Hull Company, Inc., of Crooksville, Ohio. "Little Red Riding Hood" items were soon in great demand - and still are today. However, the A.E. Hull Company did not trim or decorate these items. Blanks produced by Hull were sent to the Royal China and Novelty Company of Chicago, Illinois, who decorated the items.

Disaster struck on June 16, 1950, when a flood and subsequent fire destroyed the plant equipment and office records, including formulas, mold designs, payroll, accounts, etc. Under the direction of J.B. Hull, on January 1, 1952, a new plant opened with the name changed to The Hull Pottery Company.

Art lines were again produced with Louise Bauer as designer. Woodland, which has been introduced prior to the disaster, was again produced but proved that the pre-1950 matte finish could not be duplicated. It was then manufactured in two tone and white high gloss colors. Subsequent art lines which were unique to themselves included: Parchment and Pine, Sunglow, Ebb Tide, Classic, Blossom Flite, Butterfly, Serenade, Royal Woodland, Fiesta, Tokay, Tropicana, and Continental. Vast numbers of novelty items including swans, banks, dogs, cats, and a wide variety of kitchenware items were also produced during the fifties.

The sixties demonstrated a production change from art lines (Tuscany) to predominately House 'n Garden serving ware and Imperial florist ware which continued through the seventies. Initially, House 'n Garden serving ware was produced in the high gloss color of Mirror Brown, but later in Tangerine, Green Agate, and Butterscotch. this combination was called Rainbow, and advertised as such in assorted colors. Crestone was another casual serving ware produced in a high gloss turquoise with white foam edge color.

In 1978 J. B. Hull died, and Henry Sulens became President, with Robert W. Hull as Chairman of the Board of Directors. In 1981 Larry Taylor replaced Sulens as the President until the factory closed in March, 1986. In the closing years, the company was plagued with multiple union strikes and competition from foreign made wares which were cheaper to produce and market. During those years, until 1985, the company continued to make dinnerware lines which included the House 'n Garden Line, the Ridge Collection, Heartland, and Blue Belle.

Today, even though the factory is closed, the many different lines produced are continually sought by an ever increasing number of enthusiastic collectors who value and love Hull Pottery.

Bauer, Louise. Personal interviews 1985-1989 & 1992.

Burks, John H. Personal correspondence.

Coates, Pamela. **Hull**

Felker, Sharon. **Lovely Hull Pottery.**

Felker, Sharon. **Lovely Hull Pottery, Book 2.**

Holmquist, Betsy. Advertisements from old magazines.

Hull, Byron. Hull Pottery plant, July 1985.

Hull, Joan. "Baskets From Hull." **The Glaze,** May 1983.

Hull, Joan. "Hard to Complete Hull's Riding Hood." **Collectors News,** May 1978.

Hull, Joan. "Hobbies as Therapy." **The Glaze,** April 1981

Hull, Joan. "Hull's Hidden Treasures." **Antique Trader Weekly,** April 22, 1987.

Hull, Joan. "Little Red Riding Hood." **Antique Trader Weekly,** January 26, 1983.

Hull, Joan. "Little Red Riding Hood: The Darling of Hull Collectors." **The Glaze,** August 1983.

Hull, Joan. **The Antique Trader Weekly:** Hull Pottery – The End and The Beginning. January 13, 1993.

Hull Pottery Newsletter, Betty and Joe Yonis

Jeromach, Paul. "An Unusual Red Riding Hood." **The Glaze,** February 1984.

Konyha, Dee. Personal Correspondence.

Kovel, Ralph and Terry Kovel. **The Kovel's Antique Price List.**

Lehner, Lois. **Ohio Pottery and Glass.**

Marshall, H.W. Personal interview, July 8, 1983.

Roberts, Brenda. **Ultimate Encyclopedia of Hull Pottery.**

Roberts, Brenda. "The Hull Pottery Closes . . . An End to Family Tradition," **The Antique Trader Weekly.** August 13, 1986.

Showers, Gladys. Private correspondence & personal interviews.

Supnick, Mark. **Collecting Hull Pottery's "Little Reding Hood".**

Tomes, Patricia A. National Association of Watch & Clock Collectors. Private correspondence, November 9, 1980.

Warman's Americana and Collectibles, Harry L. Rinks, editor.

Warman's Antiques, Harry L. Rinks, editor.

Whitehouse, Don. Personal interview, 1992.

Joan Gray Hull was born in Oklahoma, and moved to South Dakota when she married Vernon W. Hull. She has a master's degree in Guidance and Counseling from South Dakota State University, and was high school counselor for 20 years. She opted for early retirement to write **HULL The Heavenly Pottery,** and to pursue other interests in collecting and working as a travel guide.

She has received numerous awards including: National Solo parent Mother of the Year, National Solo Parent President, South Dakota Counselor of the Year, and was the 1985 South Dakota Mother of the Year.

Widowed at an early age, she raised four daughters. When asked about her children, she usually quips, "They are all grown, educated, happily married, gainfully employed, and they don't call home collect." The daughters have presented Joan with six grandchildren (so far): Erikka, Erinn, Jill, Jon, Jade, and Cole.

Mrs. Hull does a great deal of public speaking and travelogues both in and out of South Dakota. She has co-authored a book with her brother, Robert Gray, **Shades of Gray,** has had articles published in the Antique Trader and The Glaze, and is the Hull price expert in **Warman's Antiques** and **Warman's Americana and Collectibles.**

SHADES OF GRAY

Shades of Gray contains over 300 anecdotal true short stories that have happened in the author's, her family's and ancestor's lives. Written with lots of humor and puns, it will keep you laughing a lot and crying a little. You can relate your own life with it's many stories, and will wish you had written the book. If you have ever thought you wanted to write a book about your family, you will want to copy this format.

Joan Gray Hull was the co-author of **Shades of Gray** with her brother, Robert Gray. You may order this delightful book for $8.95 plus $2.00 shipping and handling from:

Joan Gray Hull
1376 Nevada S.W.
Huron, South Dakota 57350
(605) 352-1685

ACME POTTERY 9
ADVERTISING 10, 63, 128
ANIMALS 20, 34, 39, 40, 1, 59, 61, 67, 94
APPLE 40
ATHENA 47
AVACADO 37
BAND 54
BANKS 39, 51, 94, 61
BELL 102, 103
BIRDS 9, 20, 45, 47, 53, 59, 81, 83, 93, 96
BLOSSOM 21
BLOSSOM FLITE 11
BLUE BIRD 13
BOUQUET 21
BOW-KNOT 15
BUTTERFLY 17
CALLA LILY/JACK-IN-THE-PULPIT 19
CAMILLA/OPEN ROSE 80-83
CAPRI 20, 45, 53
CEREAL WARE 13
CINDERELLA/BLOSSOM & BOUQUET 21
CLASSIC 23
CLOCKS 23, 69
CONTINENTAL 25
CONVENTIONAL ROSE 13
COOKIE JAR 25, 35, 41, 63
CRAB APPLE 26
CRESCENT 27
CRESTONE 28
DAISY 35
DEBONAIR 29
DOGWOOD/WILD ROSE 31
DUCKS 25, 53
EARLY ART 97-99
EARLY UTILITY 97-101
EBB TIDE 32, 93
EXPERIMENTALS 12, 77, 93, 94, 95, 118, 119
FANTASY 33, 45, 47, 49, 50
FIESTA 34
FISH 32, 93
FLORAL 35
FOAM EDGE 29, 33, 37, 39, 41, 43-49, 93
GRANADA 37
GRAPES 106
GEESE 53
HAND PAINTED 128
HERITAGEWARE 37
HOUSE 'N GARDEN 37, 39, 41, 51, 91
HUMAN FIGURES 9, 55, 107
IMPERIAL 43-55
IRIS/NARCISSUS 57, 60, 93
JACK-IN-THE-PULPIT/CALLA LILY 19
LAMPS 55, 58, 59, 54, 65, 85, 89, 91, 109
LEEDS BOTTLES 61

LIQUOR BOTTLES 61
LITTLE RED RIDING HOOD 10, 59, 62-70
LUSTERWARE 71
MADONNA 55
MAGNOLIA, GLOSS 73
MAGNOLIA, MATTE 75
MARCREST 76
MARDI GRAS 37
MAYFAIR 47
MISCELLANEOUS 36, 43-55
MORNING GLORY 77, 94
NARCISSUS/IRIS 57
NOVELTY 51-55
NULINE BAK-SERVE 79
OLD SPICE 79
OPEN ROSE/CAMELLIA 81-83
ORCHID 41, 59, 85
PAGODA 86
PARCHMENT AND PINE 45, 86
PEOPLE 9, 55, 107
PINECONE 20, 87
PLAIDWARE 41
PLATES 9, 15, 94
POPPY 89
RAINBOW 90
RED RIDING HOOD 10, 59, 62-70
REGAL 47, 49
ROSELLA 59, 91-93
ROYAL 53, 93
SALT AND PEPPER 25, 35, 39, 65, 103
SAMPLES 12, 77, 93, 94, 95, 118, 119
SERENADE 96
SHELLS 32, 47, 49
SHADES OF GRAY 125
SHULTON 79
STONEWARE 97, 101
STRIPED 25
SUENO (TULIP) 109
SUNFLOWERS 35
SUNGLOW 102
SUPREME 103
SWANS 20, 53
THISTLE 103
TILE 104
TOKAY 43, 106
TRILLUM/WILDFLOWER 113-117
TROPICANA 107
TULIP 58, 59, 109
TUSCANY 106
VEGETABLE 43
WATER LILY 60, 111
WILD FLOWER 113-117
WILD ROSE/DOGWOOD 31
WOODLAND 47, 93, 117, 118
ZANE GREY 120

Hull pottery designer, Louise Bauer, pictured in her charming home, is holding a Parchment & Pine basket she designed. Louise began contracting her artwork to the Hull Pottery Company in 1949 and continued designing until the plant closed in 1986. She designed Bow Knot, Woodland, Little Red Riding Hood, Serenade, Ebb Tide, Butterfly, Blossom Flite, Tokay, Tropicana, and hundreds of other novelty items, vases, and patterns, including Hull's famous Gingerbread Man.

Perfect Setting for Favored Flowers
HULL'S
New Magnolia

An art pottery masterpiece, with a beautifully hand-painted sculptured floral decoration . . . made enduringly lovely, forever lustrous under a rich glaze of transparent pink. Twenty-four smart pieces at your favorite store; crafted by THE A. E. HULL POTTERY Co., CROOKSVILLE, OHIO.

IT'S THE LOVELY
New Magnolia
STYLED BY HULL

You'll say, too: "What lovely art pottery!" For *New Magnolia* is all of that with its twenty-four graceful pieces . . . its rich, hand-painted floral . . . its overall glaze of subdued pink. Women everywhere are choosing it to brighten their homes, to add extra beauty to their favorite flowers. See it now at your favorite store.

Crafted by the Master Potters of
THE A. E. HULL POTTERY CO.
Crooksville, Ohio

Rosella

Accentuate the beauty of your favorite flowers with ROSELLA vases. Distinctively designed by Hull master craftsmen; with the sculptured wild rose pattern hand-tinted under the glaze on a choice of ivory or coral body. Sixteen smart shapes at better stores everywhere . . . Rosella folder on request to A. E. Hull Pottery Co., Crooksville, Ohio.

HULL
Modern Art Pottery